David:

In case you find
yourself in the mood
for more Chinese
strangeness — YA
style.

Best Yj & John

EMPRESS WU BOOKS

Published by Empress Wu Books

Library of Congress Control Number: 2021903819

ISBN 978-1-953124-06-7

ZHIGUAI

CHINESE TRUE TALES OF THE PARANORMAL AND GLITCHES IN THE MATRIX

VOLUME I

EDITED AND TRANSLATED BY

YI IZZY YU & JOHN YU BRANSCUM

"I, Zhuangzi, once had a dream that I was a butterfly. Flashing here, flitting there, I thought vivid butterfly thoughts. I saw everything in the world as a butterfly might. I felt butterfly joy and butterfly self-awareness. I had no idea that there was a man named Zhuangzi. But then suddenly I awoke, quick as a clap, a man who knew he was a man named Zhuangzi. Now, I ceaselessly wonder: What am I really? A man who dreamed he was a butterfly? A butterfly now dreaming it is a man? The man and the butterfly must be different things. Yet, they must be the same thing too. This is the mystery known as the transformation of things."

—Zhuangzi (369–286 BCE)

*For George Alleman, John Alleman, Liam Alleman, Durra Alshareefy,
Masah Alshareefy, Mukhtar Alshareefy, Francesca Branscum, Ona
Brown, 曹源, Wyn Farrington, Zo Farrington, Amiya Kesari, Yian
Kesari, 刘恩彤, 刘劲杨, 刘秦睿, 刘悦杨, Kaysi McGhen, Aidan
O'Donnell, Athena Yang, Audrey Yang, Evan Porter, Noah Porter, Lucy
Powers, Charles Quinten Ratay, Olivia Marie Ratay, Charlotte Sadler,
James Sadler, Bernie Schwab, Yongge Schwab, Boyd Schwab, Fawn
Sorrell, Heath Sorrell, Willow Sorrell, Mia Streets, Vivianne Tabbutt,
Bright Tchekpassi, James Tchekpassi, Madelyn Vetter, Helena Wender,
Ira Wender, and 苑艺.
Live in wonder.*

CONTENTS

INTRODUCTION

Sometimes, the world turns strange:

You stumble into a cracked-mirror version of reality, filled with eerie light and twisted versions of people you know—or inhabited by strangers whose slightest, icy touch causes frostbite and tissue damage.

In the middle of the day, every living thing except you eerily disappears from your busy office building, leaving you temporarily trapped in a deserted pocket of time and space.

You catch a strangely dressed man lurking around your neighbor's home, fast-forwarding and cycling through hue and saturation like video feed.

Or time loops, slows, quickens, or seems to run backward, while messages from the future arrive and prove accurate.

Mandala effects. Parallel Universes. Doppelgangers. Mind-matter interaction. Communication with the discarnate. In the Western world, nonfiction tales that center on such things are known as "glitch-in-the-matrix" stories, a term that comes from the 1999 science fiction movie *The Matrix* and which has come to mean any personal experience that makes us question the nature of reality or our ability to know it.

Although these frequently fill us with awe, such experiences can be deeply unsettling and horrifying as well. Even more than those that take place within horror fiction. Because the people sharing them—faces pale, voices shaking—swear that they actually happened.

These tellers are often hard to dismiss. They have reputations for honesty and level-headedness. Or there are other eyewitnesses involved. But mostly their stories are convincing because of what's in their eyes: a far-away, bombed-out quality that comes from confronting the impossible.

Still, most people work hard to dismiss their stories. Because if they are true, well then the world is not what we think, is it? Or time. *We* might not even be what we think we are.

So detractors shove these glitch tales away like a "wrong" thing, a diseased thing, frightened at a deep primal level of their being. They grasp frantically for any reason to dismiss them. "Hah!" they say, for example. "If such things really happened, wouldn't people all over the world have similar stories?"

Here's the thing. People all over the world do. They always have. And in China, such tales are known as "zhiguai" which translates to something like "records of the strange."

In ancient times, zhiguai were highly regarded—especially by historians and philosophers. It was thought that they could teach you about secret dimensions of reality, important cosmic laws, your own untapped potential, or what was sometimes referred to as "shendao," [神道] the way of spirits.

While today, zhiguai are most well known because of their influence on the plots of modern supernatural and horror fiction, they still also continue to exist in the form of autobiographical weird stories that are shared furtively between people. They're whispered about in school yards and workplaces, discussed in Taoist and Buddhist temples, inspire artists and scientists, and are shared with friends at night market cafes or are posted on internet bulletin board threads devoted to the strange.

The collection of modern zhiguai you are about to read gathers together in one place some of the eeriest and most haunting of these modern weird true tales. You'll find them shockingly similar to not just ancient Chinese accounts but also to modern Western counterparts. In this, they suggest that Easterners and Westerners frequently encounter the same strange dimensions of reality and have since time began.

On the other hand, you'll be fascinated by the cultural differences you come across: differences in food, relationships, education, attitudes toward the elderly, in holidays, and in religious and magical practices. And don't be surprised if you encounter your own glitch after reading this book by the way. That's one of the magical qualities of glitch stories. They entertain, sure. They disturb and fill you with awe. But they also open your eyes and ears to what wasn't noticed before, and act as magnets for the strange in your own life.

You'll see.

YEYE'S GIRL

OHNE RE

In China, many people believe that the dead visit their loved ones, especially shortly after death. Sometimes when they do, they hurt the living. They don't mean to. But dying is a big shock, and the minds of new ghosts are often cloudy and damaged. Even those new ghosts who retain their wits can accidentally hurt you.

In my family, for example, the ghost of my yeye [grandfather] would sometimes visit one or the other of us. We could always tell who he had come to see because that person would get violently nauseous, and their stomach would hurt in a very particular way. This, my grandmother said, was a result of ghosts being made mostly of yin energy, while human beings were made mostly of yang energy.

Whenever we would suspect my grandfather might be visiting, we would do "the chopstick test" to make sure. This is where you stand three chopsticks up in a bowl of water, while calling out the name of a spirit that you suspect is in the room. If they are in the room, after you remove your hands from the chopsticks, they will remain standing. I saw this happen several times. It was very unsettling. The following story is even more so. —YIY

When I was three and a half, my yeye drank pesticide and killed himself. To understand why, you first have to know this: from the day I was born, Yeye loved me dearly. He fell in love with me, he said, as soon as he saw my tiny face. And on that very day, he asked my parents to move in so that he could watch me while they worked.

In China, it is common for one grandparent or another, or even an aunt or an uncle, to move in with new parents to help look after children. But my grandfather had a characteristic that worried my parents. He was addicted to liquor and drank it every day. A lot of it. Because of this, my father denied Yeye's request.

Yeye's feelings were hurt but not enough to quit drinking. Not at first. After all, my dad still let me stay with him and my grandmother during the Lunar New Year and Autumn Festival holidays. So for a while, he was able to have liquor and me both.

However, my parents eventually started to worry about this unsupervised time too. And my dad picked me up from these visits earlier and earlier.

When Yeye noticed that our time together was dwindling, he devised a strategy to avoid my father. As soon as he saw my father's car, he would hoist me on his back and race up the mountainside behind his house to hide and play until my dad gave up looking for us.

But Yeye knew his trick would not last forever. After all, my dad could just refuse to drop me off. So finally Yeye did it.

He went to my parents and solemnly promised not to drink liquor anymore.

At first, my parents didn't believe him. But when he didn't touch a drop for several weeks, they talked. Afterwards, my father called Yeye and told him that he could move in for a year and watch over me. And he could begin this new role on his birthday. That would be their present to him.

Yeye's eyes filled with tears at the news. He was so full of excitement that it was very hard for him to wait until his birthday. Nevertheless, he managed to be patient until the day arrived.

But then the whole plan fell apart.

It happened like this:

My third uncle, who ran a bus business, was supposed to drive the couple of hours to my yeye's village and then get him to our apartment in time for Yeye's birthday celebration and his first night as my caretaker.

That *was* the plan.

But my uncle started in a game of cards with friends early that morning and got lost in that. By the time he remembered that he was supposed to pick up Yeye, it was too late.

Today, of course everyone would be constantly calling everybody else to check on everything.

But this all happened before there were cell phones. True, we were one of the few families with a landline. But we could only afford one. And my dad kept it in his office, which was located in another apartment in our building.

That's why when it started getting so late that something was obviously wrong, my dad decided to walk to my uncle's. He thought that maybe my uncle had misunderstood the plan and driven Yeye to his place and was waiting on us. Just before my dad got out of the building, the phone in his office began ringing—over and over—and would not stop. When he answered it, he heard my grandmother's voice.

"Your father's gone," she said.

* * *

My yeye waited for my uncle a long time.

He waited until he became convinced that no one was coming for him and that my dad had changed his mind.

Sad that he'd lost my dad's trust again, and his chance to be with me, Yeye drank a glass of alcohol. Then another—all the while crying his heart out.

When the alcohol didn't dull the pain, he drank a bottle of pesticide.

My grandmother watched him drink the pesticide—but she thought he was just drinking more alcohol. Even when she went out a little later to go shopping and came across him completely still on a sofa, she just thought he had fallen asleep. But then she came back home and tried to shake him awake.

* * *

The first seven days after Yeye died were filled with funeral preparations. My mom had to use up all her sick days from work to get everything done. My dad was very busy with the preparations too. So neither of them had much time to look after me. That's why, on one of these days, they sent me to a daycare.

I seemed okay when my father dropped me off that morning. But when he came to pick me up later, he couldn't wake me. Not completely. I'd mumble and stir but immediately drowse off again.

Worried, he asked the daycare attendant how long I had been sleeping.

"For most of the afternoon," she said. "I know because she was asleep during snack time and also asleep when her grandfather visited."

The attendant then told my father that she was so concerned by my deep sleeping that she asked the daycare nurse to take a look at me. The nurse said that I was probably just catching a cold, and my body was fighting it off.

The attendant's words didn't make my father feel better. Not only did he still find my deep sleeping strange, but the comment about my grandfather visiting unsettled him. Since his father was now dead, this grandfather had to be my mother's dad. But neither my dad nor my mom had mentioned that they were going to drop me off at the daycare to anyone. So how did my mom's father know I was there? And why had he even visited?

Confused, my dad asked the attendant what my grandfather looked like.

She gave him a long, careful description that included the wearing of a unique, black fedora.

When she was done talking, my dad was so shocked he couldn't breathe.

She had described his dead father, my yeye, perfectly.

My dad rushed me home. He and my mom tried everything to wake me.

Pushing pressure points.

Slapping my feet.

Pricking my middle fingertips with an acupuncture needle.

Nothing worked.

That's when they began to suspect my problem was related to the daycare visit by my yeye's ghost and decided to carry me to a psychic.

The psychic confirmed their worst fears. "Yes," she told them. "You're correct. Your daughter's problem is her grandfather. He's attached himself to her. He loves her very much. So he doesn't mean harm. Nevertheless, the attachment is draining your daughter's strength."

Frightened, my parents begged for the psychic's help. She agreed but said that she couldn't help until the next morning. That's when the sun was powerful enough to give her the yang energy she needed to fight the ghost.

When morning came, the psychic set up a square table in our living room. She sat in front of it, mediating and chanting, while my father—per her directions—walked around in our yard, holding a black umbrella while shouting my name. After they'd done this for a bit, the psychic took a chicken out of a wooden carrier. She cut its head off and used the bloody neck stump to paint magical symbols on a stack of yellow papers. These she pasted all over the house. When the last of them was glued to the wall, I woke up. Just like that.

The unhealthy bond between my yeye's ghost and me was now broken, the psychic explained. But I would still be vulnerable for a long time to ghostly influences. So the paper talismans should stay on our walls. We took the psychic's advice and kept the talismans up until the day I turned eight years old.

* * *

Some people question whether the psychic and her rituals really helped. Maybe I would have woken up anyway, they say.

Maybe.

But I'm convinced that they worked. This is because of what I remembered when I awoke.

After Yeye walked into the daycare that day, he led my spirit away from my sleeping body to a Western-style carnival (It's important to say here that all of this was very real and not like a dream. To this day, for example, I can still recall how things felt, tasted, and smelled at the carnival).

The carnival surprised me. I had never seen it before in our town. And, at this time of my life, I had never even been to a carnival or encountered one on TV (This was 1993. Just like phones, televisions were still rare and so were Western-style carnivals).

Nevertheless, I had a really good time there.

I ate a big strawberry candy, rode on a Ferris wheel, then in a bumper car, and finally on a giant car-shaped ride that swung in the air.

But there was one bad thing. Or at least strange.

The weather.

Ever since Yeye and I left the daycare, the sky looked wrong. It was an odd, ashy gray—stained with purple. A very scary kind of color, as if a big storm was about to break.

It didn't rain though. So we kept playing and eating delicious food.

But even carnival fun can last too long. And after what felt like two days passed, I was so exhausted that I could barely stand.

When I complained to Yeye that I was tired, he hoisted me on his back and took a couple of steps forward.

Suddenly, we were no longer walking on the carnival grounds but on the mountain road next to his and my grandmother's house. Trees lay to the sides of the road. Icicles hung from several of them, and Yeye and I took turns snatching them off the branches and eating them like popsicles (People in the mountains did this all the time when I was a kid).

I had just about finished one of these tree-sicles when abruptly I found myself back at my parent's place, fully awake, my opened eyes taking in my parents, the psychic, and the talismans all over our walls.

This is how I know the rituals really helped.

* * *

After I woke up that day, I rarely saw my yeye—just a dream every year or so. Three dreams were especially vivid. I think these might have been actual visits.

In one, Yeye was digging a hole in the ground—a deep one as tall as a person. When he looked up from his work and saw me, he handed me some candies.

"Why are you digging?" I asked him.

He told me the hole was part of a highway and that he was part of a work crew. There were other kinds of work that he could have chosen. But the highway construction project was the closest project to me that he could get. He intended to stay on it another twenty years. That way, he said, he could watch out for me.

The second dream I had occurred when I was grown up and just starting college in another city—far from where I and Yeye had once been so close.

In this dream, I was walking across a field when I suddenly came across Yeye sitting on a stone seat outside a yard with super high walls.

"What are you doing here outside the wall?" I said.

Yeye told me that someone had cut down the shade tree near his house and so he was sitting under the wall to get some shade.

The next day I called my mom and told her about the dream. She said it was just a random dream and not to be so serious about it. But then a few days later, she called me back.

"Your dream meant something," she said. It turned out that my fourth aunt 's husband had cut down the tree in front of the grandpa's grave.

The most recent dream happened in 2015. It was different from all the others. While I could hear Yeye's voice, I couldn't see him. It was like he and I were standing in a large, dark room.

"I have to leave you, little one," he told me. "It's time for us to let each other go. You have to look out for yourself now. Don't fight this. It is the right thing."

I promised him I would do my best to let go. Since then I have not dreamed of him once.

My yeye really, truly, so deeply loved me. Even more than my dad. No matter his faults, he constantly showed me this.

If I wanted candy, he would buy a big box and then another big box.

If I wanted to eat watermelon, he would get one of those big, twenty-five pound ones.

If I wanted clothes, he would buy me three outfits and let me switch from one to the other—all on the same day.

Sometimes, his generosity drove my dad crazy. He would yell at me for asking Yeye for so many things. At those times, Yeye would jokingly chase my dad out into the street and threaten to beat him with a stick for scolding me.

Once, a chicken that Yeye raised scratched me. The next thing I knew the chicken was cooked into a soup for me. He never raised any more chickens in his yard after that. My dad sometimes says that if Yeye were still alive, I would have turned out to be a spoiled, rotten girl. I'm not certain that is true.

Anyway, it's approaching midnight now. I miss my yeye. That's all I wanted to say.

A JUMP OFF THE BUS

ZHONG ZHONG

Fortune telling is very popular in China. Before weddings and other important events, people visit a fortune teller to find out the best date for the event. They go see specialists who interpret their dreams. They do tea leaf readings at home. There are a lot of professional psychics who make money this way. But sometimes you don't need a specialist. You don't need to do any kind of ceremony. A vision just comes to you. Frequently, this occurs right before a death or something else terrible.
—*JYB*

The incident I'm going to tell you about occurred a few years ago, shortly after I moved to the city to look for a job. It still chills me when I think about it.

One day, I had an interview. I used the app *Baidu Map* to see what bus to take to the interview site. I discovered that the ride was unfortunately going to take about an hour, but I found the appropriate bus pretty easily and boarded. I didn't grab a seat—those were all full—but instead stood, bracing myself in place with the help of the overhead bar.

I had been standing for about six or seven stops when suddenly a sharp pain—so bad it almost knocked me down—punched me in the stomach.

It wasn't an "I need to go to the bathroom" kind of pain or a food poisoning kind of pain. It was pure panic. It began from my stomach, but from there it icily pulsed throughout my whole body, causing my heart to hammer, my mind to flood. I felt—KNEW—something horrible was about to happen and that I had to immediately get off the bus.

I stumbled quickly up to the driver. "Hey, can you stop?" I said, trying to control my voice so I didn't sound like a lunatic. "I need to breathe some fresh air for a minute."

The bus driver laughed. "This is a bus,' he said. "And you're not the only passenger on it. All these people need to get somewhere. There's no way I'm going to stop just so you can have a rest. Are you crazy?"

The driver expected me to sit down then and feel ashamed for acting precious. But there was no way I was going to do that. The panicked feeling was even stronger now. Like a gun pointed at my head.

"Stop!" I shouted as loud as I could. "Stop the bus! Do it now! Or everything will be destroyed!"

All the other passengers heard me. Several whispered I must be unhinged. But I didn't care. And seeing that the bus driver still wasn't listening, I yelled even louder. "Stop! Or I'm going to jump out the window!"

I turned, as if about to do just that.

Understanding now that I was serious, that there was no

persuading me to back off, and that I was maybe even danger-ous, the driver slammed the brakes so hard that the bus squealed.

Seconds later, two trucks in front of us collided at an upcoming intersection.

The vehicles exploded with a boom. Fire shot up in the sky, and the front of the bus crumpled like tin foil from the force of the explosion, causing the bus to rock and spin violently.

There was shrieking and crying, and everyone was sure they were about to die. But then the bus became still again, and they understood. They understood I'd just saved their life by getting the driver to stop the bus when he did. If I hadn't, we would have collided with the trucks and been incinerated or blown to pieces.

People gathered around me, saying thank you over and over again and crying.

I just stood there, in shock at what happened. In shock that some power had been hiding inside me this whole time that could predict the future.

That day is one of the things I'm most proud of in my life. I am proud that I was brave and spoke up. If I hadn't, things might have turned out just like I foretold: everything destroyed and everybody on the bus dead.

THE KING OF CATS

KEN DE

The cat has historically been highly regarded in China, so much so that hundreds of thousands of cat paintings and poems have been produced over the centuries, as well as essays on the cat's sharp intelligence, its fierce independence, and supernatural abilities. In fact, in ancient China the cat was so respected that when someone decided to adopt a kitten, they first brought the mother cat small toys or fish to obtain her blessing.

Today, just like in ancient China, many people believe that cats have special powers. It is thought that they can see ghosts, scare away evil spirits, and attract good fortune. The belief is so prevalent that many businesses position a special cat figurine called "zhao cai mao" [招财猫] at their entrances to bring good luck and fortune. However, the luck portrayed in the following account is not the good kind. —YIY

I n 1994, when I was 12 years old, I was kind of the king of our apartment complex. As soon as I went outside, seven or eight children would rush up to me to play.

We did everything you can think of that kids will do—walking on the tops of stone walls and roofs, climbing trees, teasing animals, roaming the woods, playing with ants, etc.

Among these children, I was closest to F.

F and I lived right next door to each other and had known each other since we were bare-butt kids. F's grandfather was an old-fashioned type, very scholarly and artistic, the sort who keeps birds as pets. At any one time, he would have around 20 in his household. Chirping, twittering, whistling, beeping, and doing the birdy things that birds do.

Since F and I got along so well, F's grandfather was very kind to me. That's why when he discovered that I liked birds too, he gave me one as a gift.

Because we lived in Northern China, it would get bitter cold in winter. The wind felt mean then, like someone pinching your face. To keep warm, people burned coal in big indoor stoves that doubled as cooking devices and furnaces. Consequently, every family had a coal shed in the outside courtyard.

Apartment numbers were written on each of these coal sheds so that you knew what coal belonged to who. These coal sheds held more than coal, however. In the winter, there were also full of feral cats, who had decided that the sheds were the best places to hide out from the cold.

For a long time, this wasn't a big deal, and none of the coal shed owners minded. The cats were easy to get along with. They caught mice and rummaged in the garbage cans for greasy bones and bits of seafood. But their population kept increasing until there was too many to keep fed this way. That's when they began to stalk pet birds.

In the summer of 1994, F's grandfather hung several birdcages in the courtyard to give their tiny inhabitants some outdoor time, something bird owners did regularly. It was kind of the bird version of walking your dog. But on this day, the cats alerted one another about the prey suspended in the air.

An hour later, we discovered their handiwork.

One cat had apparently launched itself straight up and latched onto a birdcage with three of its legs. It then used the paw of a fourth leg to grab a bird and bite it to death through the bars.

Two more birds had also been attacked. They had no wounds, but both—cold and still in the bottom of their cages —had obviously been scared to death. The rest of the birds, while very frightened, had not been harmed.

Hoping this was a one-time occurrence, a few days after this, F's grandfather nervously hung his birdcages out again. Another bird died, a quite expensive one this time.

The deaths of his birds hit F's grandfather hard. Very hard. For two days, he could not eat a thing.

Seeing him like this made me sad. But I could not fully feel the depths of his grief until two days later. That's when the cats got to my pet bird.

When I saw the tiny body, bloody and broken, it was the most devastating thing I had felt in my life up to that point. My family was very strict about my studies and controlled how I spent my time at home—so almost all of it went to my studies. No TV. No games. No long phone conversations with friends about anything but homework.

That's why they never bought me a pet themselves, although I begged and hinted. They didn't want anything in our house to distract me. I had given up hope of ever having a pet of my own when F's grandfather surprised me with my little bird. From the moment I cupped its body in my hands, it was the most precious thing in the world to me. I loved it.

But now it was dead. And the sight of that pitiful corpse set my heart on fire.

I felt rage.

I felt pain.

I felt the need for revenge.

That's why I began to kill cats.

Some were killed by a crossbow I made. Some I poisoned. Others I beat to death with bricks, sticks, or by grabbing them by the tail and slamming them against the dirt or concrete.

Countless cats died at my hands.

One day, my friends and I cornered a grown-up cat in a coal shed and began to smack it around with sticks.

Usually, when we cornered a cat, it would hiss and dodge and run around, trying to escape.

Not this cat.

It stood its ground no matter how bloody we beat it. Back arched, staring defiantly as the stick knocked it off its feet again and again—this little cat facing off against some kids that must have looked like giants.

The cat's courage was very weird to me. Impressive even. But this did nothing to lessen my rage. And I continued to beat at it as violently as I could. Within minutes, it was dead and no longer looked very much like a cat.

Afterwards, my friends and I stepped over the body to quickly glance at the back of the coal shed. That's when we discovered them.

Two kittens, obviously so young that they had just learned how to stand and walk.

We understood then. The cat had stood its ground to protect these kittens. It knew it couldn't win. But it hoped to use its death to distract us from its offspring.

When I realized this, something unclenched in my heart. I signaled to my friends to leave the kittens alone. Later, one ducked back into the shed to take a kitten home as a pet. After this incident, I never killed another cat.

Three days later, I had a dream. I was walking in the stairway of our apartment building. The stairway was very long, so long that it seemed to endlessly ascend into the sky. It was very dark too. Nevertheless, I kept walking up, hoping for an exit.

Suddenly, I heard a cat screeching and yowling—one cat, two, and then they were all around me. The sounds of big cats and small, crying softly, screaming as if dying, hissing and hiccuping and gasping. The sounds were so close and so everywhere that it seemed I was moving through a soft tunnel made of their tortured bodies.

I wasn't scared though. Instead, I was flooded with heart-broken grief, the kind that comes from the deepest center of you but at the same time seems like an endless, black ocean in which you're drowning.

All of my organs felt bruised. But especially my heart.

When I touched my face, I found I was crying.

Then suddenly I awoke. It was 3am. My pillow was wet with tears and snot. I sat up in bed and hugged my knees. There I stayed, thinking of all the horrible things I had done to the cats until morning.

But that wasn't the end of the story.

Not long after this, I got home late one night. Around ten. It was dark outside by this time of course. And it was even darker in our apartment building because the lights in the stairway were broken. I couldn't even see my hands in front of me.

Still, I managed to stumble and bump my way to the third floor. That's where I suddenly felt a blast of cold and heard a meow in the dark.

It was not loud, but it was clear.

My heart leaping into my throat, I looked toward the direction of the sound.

By this time, my eyes had adjusted to the dark, and I could see a bit, helped along by light leaking beneath some of the doors. That is how I saw it: the shadow of an animal on the landing between the third and fourth floor stairs.

It had a cat's face and cat's body, except it was more dog-sized than cat. And it had no tail. It was more like an exaggerated drawing of a cat that was missing a detail here and there than an actual cat.

Yet, it was real.

The sight of such a thing terrified me. But before I could try to get away, it rushed straight for me, barreling aggressively.

I was sure the cat thing would hit me. But right before it

reached my body, it disappeared.

Snap. Gone.

Feet like ice, hands shaking, I ran to our apartment and fumbled with the lock and door until I spilled inside.

I thought the ordeal was over then, but it wasn't.

A few hours later, I was awoken by fever that came out of nowhere.

I kicked off my sweat-drenched sheets and took a couple of breaths. From outside our apartment building, cats were meowing from every direction. Not one meow from here or one from there. But they seemed to be coming from the whole earth and the entire sky. They just went on and on and would not stop.

Panicked and certain that something was terribly wrong, I found my mom and told her about the cat thing on the stairway. Immediately, she rushed off to my grandma's house and borrowed a peach wood sword that she then hung over my bedside to work its magic.

Two days later, the fever died down.

For my entire life, what I did to those cats in the courtyard has haunted me. I know what I did was murder, and I feel the sin of it. All creatures have spirits. My strange dream, and the mirroring of it in our apartment building that night, proved this. I knew in my heart that these events were a communication from the cats I'd murdered to show me how sad and fearful they felt before they died.

After the fever was over, I tried to atone for my sins. I began to carry a little bit of cat food every day to feed stray cats.

Usually, the stray cats that hung around apartment buildings didn't hesitate to run up if they thought you had food. But what I had done was not easily forgotten. Those little ones would run away when they saw me. Even if I put the food near them, they wouldn't approach and eat—not while I was watching. This made me feel deeply ashamed.

It was like this for years. Meanwhile, I grew up. I finished school and got a job.

Then one day after I got off work, I heard some mewling in a green bush right outside my apartment. Bending down to the bush, I saw something beneath it.

A kitten. Just a few months old. Peering up at me from beneath the bush, it looked thin and hungry but wasn't afraid of me. Staring boldly in my eyes, it meowed repeatedly until I picked it up. It then happily let me carry it home.

That was nine years ago.

Since it moved in with me, that cat has loved me and treated me like a king. And I have treated it the same way. If it indicates it wants something, I immediately get it.

When I first got married, my wife told me that she was afraid of cats and asked me to send away my cat friend. No way, I told her. And we've all found a way to live together.

It's been a lot of years since I was a killer of cats. My guilt is not gone, but it has steadily decreased and the stray cats in our community no longer flee from my shadow.

What can I say?

My awe for all life just keeps growing the older I get. I know every creature out there has a heart and a spirit, that it feels love and pain. We can't just kill other creatures as if they were nothing, as if ripping pieces of paper. Not if we don't want to unbalance the world and welcome chaos.

A STUDENT VISITS THE FUTURE

CAROLINE JIU

When we think about who we were in second grade or as a baby or even last week, we assume all our old selves have somehow dissolved into who we are now, similar to how a ball of clay can be reshaped from an ashtray to a cup. But what if this isn't the case? What if those past selves stay around? The account below explores exactly that. —JYB

The following experience occurred in 2016, when I was in eighth grade, shortly before my classmates and I were scheduled to take our high school entrance exams.

This was a very hectic and stressful time. Everyone was worried about the exams. Additionally, our classes were moved into a whole new building because our usual building was now being used as a test center.

Our days were very long too. Since exams were coming up, after day classes were finished, we took a short afternoon break and then had to return to school until late into the night to study for the exams.

After one such night study session, just as everyone was preparing to leave, a girl a couple of rows in front of me started acting upset.

At first, I ignored the girl. I was focused on studying, and I didn't want to be nosy. But when she started crying, I went over to see if I could help. Several other students went to check on her too. When we asked what was wrong, she pointed to her deskmate, a guy that we all knew well—since we'd all been classmates since we were little kids. The girl said he'd lost his memory.

Initially we thought the guy was joking around. But we could tell something was actually wrong when he spoke. Wearing a lost expression, he asked us in a frightened way what he was doing in this room and why we all looked so different.

We asked him what the heck he was talking about. That's when he insisted that he was a sixth-grader—not the eighth-grader we knew him to be. According to his memory, a few minutes before he put his head down to rest. When he raised it again, everything was different. Our room. The seating order. Worst of all, the whole student body looked strikingly older.

Still not quite believing him, we asked a lot of questions about sixth grade. We figured that if he couldn't answer them then he was messing around with us. But he correctly described our seating arrangement in sixth grade. And when we asked him who his girlfriend was, instead of naming the girl he was currently dating, Tang, he answered just as he would have in sixth grade. He said that he did not have a girl-friend, but if he could have one it would be Xue (the girl he had a crush on in sixth grade).

Confused and scared, we walked our classmate to our home teacher's office. By the time we got there, he had degenerated even further and ceased to speak in our dialect. While strange, this change made sense because he was originally a transfer student from Guangdong and hadn't learned our dialect until seventh grade.

For the whole night, this incident was all we could talk about. However, when the boy recovered the next day, most people put it very quickly out of their mind. There were, after all, very important exams to take.

Me though? I couldn't stop thinking about what happened. It is incredible to me that part of this boy's memory temporarily disappeared that night. Even more incredible is the fact that all the other selves we've ever been don't entirely disappear or fade into old memories. Instead, they remain hidden inside us, alive and waiting for the chance to get out.

NOT THAT BROTHER

SAM CHAN

Most people are familiar with reincarnation these days. The basic concept is pretty simple. Post-death, your soul, or a fragment of it, is reborn in a new body. Thanks to Buddhism, this belief is very wide-spread in China. Even in America, 33% of people believe in rein-carnation.

In fact, there's a Division of Perceptual Studies at the University of Virginia Medical School that studies reincarnation.

This division, which is spearheaded by Dr. Jim Tucker, focuses particularly on reincarnation in children. Memories of former lives fade as one grows older. As a result, adults usually can't provide significant details about former lives. Children, however, can sometimes provide specific details that can be corroborated by the relatives of the deceased. Thanks to his research, Dr. Tucker has discovered a few characteristics of past life accounts that connect to the story shared below.

One, those who remember former lives usually died traumatically or unexpectedly.

Two, people who are reborn sometimes have similar birthmarks to

birthmarks they had in their previous lives or that mimic injuries asso-
ciated with their deaths.

The following story includes one further characteristic as well, one
that is more commonly found in Chinese accounts of reincarnation than
Western ones. It is the concept that certain fates can follow us around
from one life to the next. —JYB

When I was in my last year of junior high school, and around fourteen years old, I became aware of a boy in the same grade.

I didn't know this boy because he was in a different class-room and Chinese schools have thousands of students. But he stood out in the crowd. He had a small black birthmark under one eye and curly hair like me.

Whenever this boy saw me at school, he would stare for a long time. I always felt that he had something to say. I thought he probably wanted to become friends because he was being bullied by other kids due to his curly hair. Having curly hair is unusual for a Chinese boy, you see.

One day in the cafeteria, I happened to sit across from this boy. So, he came up to me.

"Does your name have the character qing (清) in it?" he asked. Chinese names, even ones that sound the same, often match up to very different characters. In fact, the pronuncia-tion of a word might correspond to any one of a hundred or more alternative characters.

"No," I replied. Then I said, "You know, I often see you

around school. So, I am not surprised that we finally spoke. But why start our conversation with such a strange question?"

He said, "Since I first saw you, I have felt like you look exactly like my brother. Except I don't have a brother. At least, this is what my parents tell me. Yet the feeling in my heart that I do have a brother is so strong that I believe it. I even know that my brother stutters. Sometimes, I remember other things too. One night during a dream, a voice talked to me about him and said that his name has the qing (清) character in it. That's why I asked you about it."

"Are you really stressed?" I asked. "Stress can sometimes cause strange thoughts and even hallucinations."

"Not really," he said. "My academic performance has always been steadily poor. So, I don't feel pressure when it comes to studying. My grades can't go much lower."

I thought over the boy's odd beliefs. Finally, I suggested that he talk to his parents again. "Just to confirm that they didn't miss telling you anything the first time you spoke that might make sense of your feelings," I said.

A few days later, school ended for that academic year, and summer vacation began.

My parents and I travelled for much of that summer. One afternoon, at a place we were staying, I mentioned the weird conversation I'd had with the boy. I repeated his question about whether or not my name had the qing (清) character in it. As I did, I realized that my dad's name in fact *does* have the qing (清) character. My dad caught this too. "Maybe he was looking for me," he joked.

My mom then started teasing my dad. She asked him if he

had neglected to tell her about having a baby with another woman.

"Did he really look like me?" my dad asked.

"No," I said. "But he does have curly hair like us. And he has a black birthmark on his face."

This last bit of information visibly stunned my dad. "Where on the face?" he asked.

"Under his eye," I told him.

His voice breaking, my dad said, "My brother also had a black birthmark under his eye. He died when he was fourteen."

The whole tone of the day shifted with my dad's revelation. The world seemed to slow down in that moment, to go quiet. Suddenly, I became aware of the heavy rain outside.

Then my mother spoke, her voice full of shock. "It's true," she said. "Your dad did have a brother. He died young from an illness."

Though she was just confirming what Dad said, my mother's words caused tears to run down his face. "How do we find this boy?" he asked.

I didn't know how to find the boy though. Because of the strangeness of our conversation in the cafeteria that day, I hadn't thought to ask his name. And his family was likely travelling for the summer like we were. It would be very difficult, if not impossible, to track him down before school started again.

After talking it over, we decided it was best to wait until the new school year started to reach out to the boy. My dad then called my grandma and, sobbing, told her that his brother might have been reincarnated. After that, we waited for what seemed like an especially long summer and discussed different ways to approach the boy and his family and exactly what to say to them.

School started in September. The first day was a check-in day. This meant that there were no classes. Instead, you went to school to meet with officials and people in administration about different concerns, and to make sure you were registered.

Because there were no classes, not all students showed up. But all the teachers did. So after I checked in, my parents, my grandparents, and my aunt figured out who the boy was and went to talk to his homeroom teacher. (We learned the boy's name, but I am not mentioning it here out of respect for his family's privacy).

However, when we explained the situation to the boy's homeroom teacher, he told us that there was no way we could meet with the boy. Nobody could. Because he was dead.

It turned out that one day that summer, while the boy was playing football on the beach, his stomach started bleeding internally, and he began coughing blood. It was one of those freak occurrences. Where you have a condition that you don't know about and find out only when it's too late. By the time the boy's family got medical help, he had already lost too much blood.

When the homeroom teacher told us about what happened, we burst out crying—right there with all the other teachers in the office area standing and staring, not believing the scene they were witnessing.

Before we left the school, the homeroom teacher gave us the boy's address, and we went to see his family.

The boy's parents heard us out.

Then they told us that ever since he was little, the boy would ask about his older brother and say that this brother's name had the qing (清) character in it. And then one day the boy came home excited because he had seen someone at school who looked exactly like this older brother: me.

The boy's parents insisted that he was perfectly normal—except for his conviction about having an older brother. So they finally decided that he must be possessed by a spirit. His mother told us, "We were going to have him looked at by a shaman, but we waited too long. And he is gone now."

She then disclosed that two days before we visited her, she dreamed of her son. He said this to her:

"After school resumes, my brother is going to visit you. When he does, ask him if his leg has fully recovered, or if it still hurts sometimes. Also, let him know I don't like the place where I am buried. See if he can help you move me behind the big banyan tree in our old village."

The boy's mother told us these things while crying.

I know that these coincidences and events seem unbelievable. But I'm now going to tell you the most unbelievable things of all, things which pull the story together and verify its truth.

A little bit after this visit, we went to see my grandmother, and she revealed crucial details about the life of my father's brother. My uncle was the only one in the whole family who went to school. But although he always worked very hard, his grades were poor. This was a big family joke.

My uncle had no other big problems, however. Especially not health problems. Or so it seemed. But one afternoon, when he was fourteen, he suddenly began vomiting blood. It was really bad, but there was no doctor in the village available to see him that night. My grandmother intended to take him to see a doctor in one of the other villages the next morning. But by then it was too late, and he died just before dawn.

My dad wasn't home when all this happened. A wild and savage seventeen-year-old delinquent with a stutter and a bad temper, he was in the habit of hanging out all night with his friends and crashing at their homes. At this time of his life, he just didn't care about much. Except for one thing: his younger brother, my uncle.

When my dad finally came home, my grandmother told him straight away what happened. His whole tough façade immediately shattered, and he stumbled around crying so hard that he fell off the stairway to the second floor and broke his leg bone.

As my grandmother revealed the detail about my dad's leg injury, I realized that this detail lined up with what the boy's mother told that he had said in her dream. A second thing lined up too: my uncle it turned out was buried behind a big banyan tree in the mountains—just like the boy said that he wanted to be in his mother's dream.

When all these incredible coincidences were revealed, my family and the boy's family knew for sure that he was my uncle's reincarnation. And we felt awed to live in a world filled with such connections.

Uncle, it turns out that I was not your brother after all. My father was.

But I am your nephew. I wish I knew when we could meet again.

TWIN DEMON

NI MING

In a way, we all talk to disembodied voices because we talk to ourselves. Even if we don't talk out loud, we talk to ourselves in our heads. We give ourselves compliments; we insult ourselves; or we argue with ourselves. In fact, it's hard to have a thought without being involved in some kind of inner conversation. When you think about the fact that we're constantly talking to ourselves as if we're a second person, this is more than a little strange. But for some people their experience of talking to disembodied voices is even stranger. Because they're not talking to themselves. —JYB

For as far back as I can remember, my twin sister has always been at my side—ready to protect me. It's hard for many people to accept this. They say that she is a delusion, and that I'm hallucinating her. In fact, when I was a kid I got sent to both a psychiatrist and a psychologist because my parents were disturbed that I kept "talking to the air."

I understand the skepticism of others. I do. But believe me. My sister exists. I'm not talking to the air. I can see her just as clearly as you see your friends. When we talk, it is the calm conversation of two different people. It is not the confused or negative talk of someone with schizophrenia. It is not like a personality split where only one personality is active in a body at a time.

I did not just invent my sister's existence either. My mother told me that when I was in her womb, I had a twin. But something went wrong, and my sister was not able to get enough nutrients from my mother's body. And so she died before she was even born.

I say "she died." But that's not quite right because her spirit stayed behind. From the time I was a toddler, it would regularly appear to me. My first memory of it is seeing a little girl my age, who greatly resembled me, standing off in the distance.

At first, my sister didn't speak. She just followed me and stared. Then one day she quit appearing as a figure in the distance in the outside world (except for a couple of times a year). Instead, she visited in my dreams. There, she would talk. These visits were usually prompted by my having a hard time. Like when I was being punished by my parents or was sick with a fever.

Later, when I was older, the nature of her visits changed again. While she would still appear in my dreams now and then, she mostly became a calm voice in my head, one that spoke even when I was awake and helped me out in times of need.

When I encountered a dangerous situation, my sister's

voice would ring out and warn me not to take this action or that.

When I took school exams and got stuck on questions, she would give me tips and hints and suggest different ways of solving test questions.

I was amazed by how much more she knew than me. This was not only true of school. She also had a way of knowing what was going on in the wider world as well. Once, for example, my grandfather became critically ill while I was attending a university in a faraway city. Somehow, my sister found out and told me to travel home and check on him. I did. When I got there, his condition was exactly as she described it.

Although the nature of my sister's visits changed as I aged, her physical appearance remained that of a little girl. Sometimes, I think how wonderful it would have been if her physical body survived inside my mother like mine did. If she grew up like I did. Then we could interact like ordinary twins rather than in the ghosty way we do. Nevertheless, I cherish the bond we have and hope it will never be broken. Maybe in the next life she can be my child. That way I can take care of her like she's taken care of me in this life. It will be my turn to protect her and show her my love.

About half a year ago, I visited Qingcheng Mountain and met with a Taoist priest. Without me telling him anything, he told me that I had a spirit protecting me.

"Keep her near," he said. "And don't do anything to scare her away. You are very lucky to have such a guardian."

Look, I'm pretty educated. I know all the alternative explanations for my situation offered by those who can't imagine that spirits exist. But their explanations only seem to make sense if you haven't had an experience like mine. If you had a chance to see my sister like I see her, if you had a chance to know her like I know her, you would have no doubt that she is real. You don't need millions of reasons to believe somebody exists when you meet them. You just do. There's nothing complicated about it.

THIRD UNCLE'S APARTMENT IS NOT HIS APARTMENT

LIU MINGWEI

In China, families commonly live in massive apartment buildings instead of houses. Newer buildings in big cities like Beijing and Shanghai can be incredibly luxurious and cutting-edge. But in small towns, some buildings date back to the 1970s when the preferred style was huge, blocky, and very plain. These prison-grey structures get little outside light and air, and their hallways and stairwells tend to be dusty and gloomy. This makes for a haunted house feeling, even in the best of times. The following account takes place in such a building. But its haunted atmosphere comes from something far more terrifying than qualities of light and air. —YIY

Around 2002, when I was in the second grade, our family had a reunion dinner during New Year's time at my third uncle's apartment. He lived on the fourth floor of a condo building—the kind that's blocky and grey. It was an easy trip to his place from my parents' place since we (my parents, me, and my grandfather) lived in the same building on the first floor.

I never liked our building. It had always seemed "off." Like certain basements or places in the woods can be off. And it was constantly cold in there during the winter months because the furnace didn't work well.

Anyway, around six or seven in the evening, I started playing outside while waiting on my mother. She had told me that she would get me when dinner was ready at my uncle's and that this would probably be around eight.

I played until it got super dark, dark enough that I was pretty sure it was well past eight, and my mother still hadn't come for me. There were street lights outside though, so I kept playing—at least I did until I got so tired that I started to think about going upstairs to my third uncle's place by myself.

It was around this time that a boy I'd never seen before approached me. He looked like he was in the fifth or sixth grade.

"Kid," he said, "let me have a look at your toy."

He was talking about the toy in my hand. It was a tiny, plastic figure meant to look like a bullet-train robot from the popular Japanese anime *Hikarian*. Exactly the kind of cheap toy surprise you find in a 50-cent bag of snacks like crispy instant noodles.

Thinking the older boy wanted to play with me, I handed him the toy.

"That too," he said, indicating my infra-red, laser-pointer (If you grew up in the 00s, you probably remember laser pointers. They were tiny, pen-shaped devices with a button that once clicked emitted a line of red light).

"No," I told the boy and explained that the laser-pointer was super precious to me. That was when he ran off with my *Hikarian* bullet-train robot, and I realized that I had been robbed.

Although this was the first time in my life I had been robbed, I immediately understood what was happening, and chased after the boy. At first, I kept up. But he kept ducking and dodging, and soon I lost him at a turn between buildings.

By this point I was crying like crazy and wanted my mom badly. So I headed inside our condo building to my parents' apartment. When I saw no one was there, I realized that they must have gone to my uncle's to get dinner ready.

So I began to climb the stairs to the fourth floor.

This was a much odder experience than I expected. The stairwell light was dimmer than usual—so dim that I held tight to the handrail in order not to trip and fall. As for the walk itself, it took an inexplicably long time. Like I was walking up far more stories than four.

Finally though, I made it to my uncle's floor and rushed to his apartment.

Almost as soon as I knocked, it jerked open—as if the opener had been standing right behind it the whole time.

The opener was my mom. But it took me a minute to recognize her. Her hair was bunched up in a style I'd never seen before. Not even on formal occasions. Still, I only barely registered the change because I was so upset by the robbery. Bursting into tears, I hugged her as hard I could. Then I told her how my toy had been snatched.

It was at this point I noticed that something was wrong with my uncle's apartment too.

He always had several lights on, each emitting bright white light from its corner. But this evening only one light was on, and its glow was strangely murky as if filtered through deep water so that it barely penetrated the room's darkness. You could make out people's faces, but not much more than that.

At first, I ignored the lack of lighting. But when we sat down at the dinner table, and they still hadn't been turned on, curiosity got the best of me.

"Why doesn't Uncle turn on the other lights?" I whispered to my dad and flashed a look at my uncle who was sitting next to his wife and my cousin Shaowei.

"*It's not your concern,*" my dad said.

His response was short, but it affected me so strongly that I flinched.

First off, his tone was weirdly fierce. Then, there were the actual words he spoke. Although he could sometimes be bad-tempered with other people, not once in my life had he ever spoken to me so dismissively.

I was so surprised and hurt that I started crying again.

At the sound of my sob, everyone at the dinner table swiveled in my direction. Not the slightest sound came from their silent bodies. Not even the sound of breathing.

And then they froze. Just like that.

Even now remembering that unnatural span of time, how their faces fell slack like rubber masks, how their bodies sat utterly unmoving, without a flicker or twitch or other sign of life, makes me tremble.

For a long time, they stayed bizarrely frozen like this until abruptly my "mother" broke her paralysis and said, "Let's eat," in a flat voice.

Instantly, as if turned on, everyone became animated: blinking and talking and shoving food in their mouths and making expressions.

Everyone except for me.

On my stool, I was too freaked out to pretend everything was normal and kept trying to think up explanations.

That was when I noticed the TV on the counter. It was on, but there was nothing playing. It was just a screen full of buzzing static like falling snowflakes.

I turned to my mother who was sitting next to me and said, "How come there's no show on the TV?"

"It's broken," she said, and my dad looked up from eating and gave me a look filled with hate—like nothing in the world would make him happier than seeing me dead.

In that moment, I knew without a doubt that both my mom and my dad weren't in fact my mom and dad at all but imposters.

I knew that everyone in the room was an imposter.

Even the light.

It was an impossible thought. Its insanity made me feel nauseous.

But I also knew it was true and wanted nothing more than to escape immediately. If I didn't, I was sure something terrible would happen to me.

However, I knew that I had to escape slyly and not be obvious about it. Otherwise, they would know that I knew and take action. So I lied.

"Mom," I said. "I was so upset when that bigger kid took

my *Hikarian* figure that I accidentally forgot my other toys in the courtyard. I'm going to go get them, okay?"

Before my mother could reply, my uncle's wife spoke up instead. "It's so dark. Let your cousin Shaowei go with you."

I didn't know exactly what this "Shaowei" might do to me, but I knew letting him go with me would be a mistake.

"No. That's all right," I said, trying to be casual, as I hopped off my stool and walked to the front door.

Everyone's eyes were on me as I crossed the room, burning into my back.

I was very afraid that someone would grab me, but no one did. So, shivering, I stepped through the door and ran downstairs as quickly as I could. I still remember my panicked feeling. It would return in nightmares during the next few years.

When I reached the second floor, the thing I was afraid of happened. I heard an upstairs door opening.

It was my uncle's door—I could tell. This scared me so badly that I shrieked and flew down the remaining stairs, to then dash outside to the nearest street.

I was desperate for a familiar face. But I saw no one that I recognized in the faces of the people I passed—at least not until I turned a corner into another street and saw my mother.

My *real* mother.

Her hair wasn't up like the other mother's had been. It was down like always. Although it was dark, I saw her facial expressions clearly enough to know that it was her for sure.

I ran up and took her arm. At first, she was angry to see me. But when she registered how terrified I looked, she became gentle.

"Where were you?" she asked. "I couldn't find you in the

courtyard. And the whole family was waiting for you to come up upstairs to start eating. When I told them you had disappeared, they all came downstairs to help me look."

I knew for sure then that I hadn't been in my third uncle's apartment at all—but rather in a copy of some kind. This knowledge set me shaking violently.

Seeing me like this, my mother went pale and called out to the rest of the family. Together, they rushed me back to our place to eat something, thinking this might help.

I didn't eat a single bite of food. Instead, I finally worked up enough courage to tell everyone what happened. Because they could see how serious I was as I spoke, no one doubted my story. My third uncle's wife even got up after I finished speaking and carried some hell money downstairs to burn outside the building.

A few years after that night, we bought a new house. And whenever an occasion arose that required us to go back to our old building, such as visiting my third uncle, I would get out of it. Just thinking about that night made me feel like I was suffocating.

I have no idea what really happened.

Did I somehow walk into a dream realm, although I was awake?

Did some kind of weird entities pretend to be my family and my uncle's apartment?

I can't answer these questions. Nevertheless, the rest of my childhood felt haunted because of that night. The details will stay with me until the day I die.

"The shadowed and the bright are two separate roads. But occasionally they cross."

—Chinese Saying

FIFTY METERS

HAN SHU

In China, many people believe that the dead live in a realm right next to ours, "the yin realm." There, they have everything we have: buildings, food, money, jobs, you name it—although these things are present in slightly different and quite odd forms sometimes.

We the living can communicate with the dead, although they are in this different realm. We do this through dreams and in places where the borders between the worlds are naturally thin. We can even send presents and necessities to the dead through burning objects and releasing their yin forms.

As well, there are people who claim to have the ability to travel to the yin realm and carry out business for the residents there. There are also other people who, when conditions are right, sometimes accidentally wander into yin realm.

When you think about it, the contemporary concept that there are parallel universes adjacent to ours fits neatly with this ancient belief. Who knows? Maybe ancient people mistook these other dimensions for lands of the dead. Or maybe we moderns are the ones mistaken. —YIY

W hen I was in third grade, my family lived in a community next to a river. It was a great place to live because during the summer I and my three friends could walk to the riverside almost every day.

We mostly hung around a narrow road that bordered the river's dam on one side—and a cemetery and a wooded area on the other. It was the kind of shaded area that might strike some people as spooky. But we were young and unafraid of graves and the dead then, and we loved how cool this area was in the summer.

Best of all, the road was the perfect place for foot racing. It was scenic, unridden by holes and ditches, and wide enough for all of us at one time. And it had two telephone poles too, sunk into the earth alongside the road, which we used to measure off our races. These were the type of wooden telephone poles that you normally see—except layered with old, weathered flyers advertising this or that. Spaced 50 meters apart, they made perfect starting and finishing lines.

One afternoon, my friends and I were racing between the two poles. The sky had abruptly darkened and turned cloudy and heavy looking a bit earlier, but we agreed to chance a downpour and stay out anyway.

I was in the middle of running, head down, legs pumping, when I felt something splatter on my cheek.

I looked up to see if it was starting to rain.

It wasn't.

But that was when I noticed to my shock that I was alone

and all my friends had disappeared. I couldn't understand how this could be. Just a second before, they were behind me. And now nothing.

Had they somehow sprinted ahead of me without my noticing? I hurried forward to the second telephone pole, the finish line, to find out. But nobody was there.

Feeling very out of sorts now, I decided to stay put and wait. Maybe my friends would appear in a few minutes and clear up the mystery. While waiting, I glanced at the telephone pole, expecting to see the same flyers I usually did. But when I looked at it, I had another shock.

All the usual flyers were gone.

Every last one.

They'd been replaced by a single, small, and very odd poster.

The poster was fancy looking, done up in the style of the God of Wealth pictures that people would post on buildings and walls during the New Year festival.

A bright red background. Gold and black words running vertically on either side of the poster.

Despite these superficial similarities though, this poster was very different from such pictures. Frighteningly different.

First, there were the characters of the words. They looked Chinese but were in fact completely indecipherable—as if written in an alien language.

And then there was the figure in the center of the poster. It wasn't the God of Wealth, but a woman sitting cross-legged on a circle of disembodied hands and lotus-like (but not quite lotus) leaves. Her eyes had dark circles beneath them, and she was smiling weirdly. The picture was so bizarre that I felt an immediate urge to rip it off the pole so I could show it to people.

Just as I felt this compulsion, someone patted me on the shoulder.

I whirled around, expecting to see one of my friends behind me. But I found an old granny instead.

She was scowling and wearing black clothing that was way too heavy for a summer day.

I touched my shoulder where she had touched it. It was warm and humid outside, but that patch of tissue now felt shockingly cold against my fingertips. Before I could think this oddity through, the old woman started reprimanding me in a very loud and alarmed voice.

"You're not supposed to be reading that," she said. "You shouldn't be here at all."

Although what she said made no sense, I felt terrified hearing it, as if I'd been caught doing something illegal by the police and now was about to be punished.

So, before she could say another word, I ran—as quickly as I could—back in the direction of the first telephone pole, where the race had first started.

Strangely, it took me forever to get there, as if somehow the distance had dramatically increased, and the space surrounding the path had been changed and become uncertain. But finally, I made it. When I arrived, I found my three friends standing around the pole.

"Where were you?" they asked.

They then explained that from their perspective I had

bizarrely vanished into the thin air before the race could begin. Although they called for me and looked everywhere, there was no sign of me. So they decided to wait at the pole.

"It was very different for me," I said. Then I told them everything: their disappearance, the weird poster, the old woman.

My story was a lot to swallow. But they agreed to go with me to the second telephone pole so we could examine the poster together.

We never made it though. Because as we began walking in that direction, someone burst out singing opera. The voice was loud and close. But we couldn't locate who was singing or where they were standing. It was very frightening and other-worldly, and one of my friends insisted we go home right away.

At my place, my mother took one look at me and said, "Were you in a fight?"

"No," I replied. "Why?"

She told me to look at my shoulder.

I pulled my shirt's neckhole open to fully expose it. There was a huge bruise along the top of my shoulder, deep and purple. It was right where the old lady had patted me, right where I noticed the freezing sensation immediately afterward. That sensation had now spread, along with the bruise, so that touching my shoulder was like touching raw ice.

I was sure I would have a severe injury, like the kind you have after really bad frostbite. But in a few days, the mark disappeared.

My memory of that day never would though. It's as fresh and clear in my mind as what happened yesterday.

My experience that day forever changed how I see reality. It woke me up to how miraculous this world of ours can be.

THE RESERVE PLAYER

AVONZEN

We naturally feel an attraction to people that are like us, don't we? People who enjoy the same music or streaming shows, who have a similar sense of humor, or like the same toppings on their pizza. Most of the time, anyway. But sometimes people can be too similar. —YIY

I n the summer of 2002, I officially became a new high school senior.

As such, I had to take classes to help prepare me for college entrance exams while all the other grade levels were on summer vacation. This meant that I and the other new seniors were the only students on campus for the next few months.

This totally changed being there. As opposed to its regular, chaotic craziness—with people streaming in all directions, talking and laughing and yelling—campus was now quiet and relaxed. Best of all, the soccer field, usually crowded with students fighting to use it, belonged to us new seniors and us alone.

We had two free hours between the regular school day and night study. These were later afternoon hours, hours at which the blistering heat of early part of the day was replaced by a more bearable temperature—the perfect time to get exercise and blow off steam.

Since the campus was half-deserted, we seniors had a lot of options to fill up those two hours: the basketball court, the running track, and about half a dozen other things. But as a super soccer fan and a devoted member of the school team, I went for the soccer field every time.

My normal routine was this: I would change into my soccer shoes during my last class. Then, the moment the dismissal bell rang, I would grab my chopsticks and empty food container and rush to the cafeteria. There, I would resist the urge to talk to the beautiful girl who always sat near me and gobble down my lunch.

Food swallowed, I would next sprint back to my dorm to drop off my utensils and grab a soccer ball. After that, I hurried to the soccer field, where I'd find my team's fans and other soccer enthusiasts already sitting and standing—ready for a show.

My team would play game after game until our two-hour break was up, after which we jogged back to our classroom, soaked in sweat, ready to start our night study session.

One night, however, I broke this routine. There was going to be a live broadcast of a big international game that I didn't want to miss. So instead of heading for the soccer field, or back to my dorm, I walked to my parent's home to use their huge TV.

I watched the game, chatted with my parents, and then returned to school for night study. That's when things got weird.

I ran into a classmate who always played soccer with me during break. He gestured to me, rolled up his pants leg, and pointed at his calf. "You got me good just now. See this bruise? That's from you kicking me while we were playing. Look how purple it is."

"What are you on about?" I said. "I didn't play today. I was home watching a live broadcast of the game."

My friend laughed, as if I was making a joke, and shot me a strange look. "Hah. Are you trying to escape responsibility? Or just messing with me? You think I can't recognize you?"

Confused, I asked a few other classmates who played my position.

They gave me the same odd look as my first friend.

"You played," one said. "You even wore your #8 jersey, the one with the colors of that English team you like so much."

Well and truly freaked out now, I pushed this classmate for further details. He revealed that not only did this other me look exactly the same, not only was he wearing my #8 jersey, but also that he had even played the same as me.

There was one difference though, he finally added. The other "me" didn't talk except for a mumble here and there. And he kept his head down most of the game, as if deep in his thoughts.

After that night, tracking down the other "me" became an

obsession. I would go to the soccer field earlier than every-body else. And I was always the last to leave for the night, hoping to catch a glimpse of myself in the jumble of the other students.

But I never saw myself. Not once.

LIGHT SWITCH

AVONZEN

Turning the lights on in a dark room is pretty amazing. There's nothing but blackness. Emptiness. And then—FWOOSH—with the flick of a switch or a wave of your hand, light floods the room and you can see everything: furniture, plants, tables, the cat. As if it all flashes into existence in that moment. It's a magical thing when you think about it. Of course, the things in the room aren't really flashing in and out of existence. Not usually. —JYB

After high school, from 2014 on, I went to work for a government agency that oversaw the maintenance of ancient funeral sites.

My office was on the first floor, where lower-level employees resided, while supervisors and big bosses occupied the second floor.

Although I didn't have access to the juicy gossip and secret information that someone with an office next to the bosses would naturally have, I was pretty happy with my job. I liked how peaceful my floor was, and how hardly anybody bothered me there.

One day I was sitting in my office and watching a movie on my laptop when suddenly a big chief on the second floor called me on the phone. There was going to be an agency-wide meeting in the second-floor cafeteria in ten minutes, he said, and he wanted me to come up. I heard several other colleagues in the background on his end of the phone call, chatting happily.

I paused the movie and left my desk. I planned to walk upstairs, duck into the big chief's office for a quick hello before the meeting, and then attend the meeting.

However, things turned weird almost as soon as I left my office.

The first-floor hallway should have been crowded with other employees also rushing to the meeting—not only from their offices on the first floor of my building, but also from the building next to ours too, which housed other employees.

But no one was coming into my building. And no one else was streaming out of their offices either. Inexplicably, I was the only one on my floor.

A deserted building is very eerie. And the sense of eeriness deepened as my footsteps echoed hollowly on my way to the stairwell. Not a single other soul was moving about.

Why was everything so abandoned? I asked myself. It made no sense.

Not once in my career had the big leaders from the other building arrived early for a meeting. So I should have heard at least one of their footsteps coming up behind me, or the sound of my building's entrance being used. Instead, the only thing that filled my ears was spectral silence. There was nothing I could do though but continue on my way to the meeting as if everything was normal. That's what I did.

I climbed the stairs to the second floor, turned to the right, and knocked on my chief's door. I was desperate for him to be there to explain away the strangeness that had taken over the building.

But there was no movement or sound inside in response to my knock.

I knocked again.

Still no response.

I pushed the door open.

No one was there.

A person's mind will always try to soothe them during threatening or confusing moments. That's what my mind did. Okay, I told myself. Don't freak out. Everything's fine. Today's meeting must be a special one, with a lot of information, and so all the supervisors and bosses went early to prepare.

I left my chief's office, walked a few steps, turned the corner, and could now see the large, wooden double doors of the cafeteria. There was no doubt my boss said the meeting would be there. But the cafeteria was obviously closed tight, although usually open during office hours—especially if a meeting was being held.

Good, I thought to myself. There *is* a meeting going on. That's why the doors are closed. And if you were to open the door right now, you would see everyone inside. You would see everything is fine.

Still, something deep inside me made me hesitate. Instead

of opening those heavy doors immediately, I decided to first open the door of a friend's office next to the cafeteria.

Just as with my boss's office, I was met again by emptiness. This time though, I smiled in relief, taking it as a sign that my friend had also gone to the meeting early. It was so clear to me that the simple explanation for all the weirdness was my boss had gotten the meeting time wrong.

I can't tell you how relieved I was that the puzzle was solved. But then I twisted the handle of cafeteria door, pushed it open, and was slammed by deserted silence, by the emptiness of a vast room without a single, beating heart.

I did some quick calculations in my head. Not more than two minutes had passed since I put down my phone, walked upstairs, and checked the offices of my boss and my friend.

Not more than two minutes could have passed since I distinctly heard not only my boss's voice but the voice of other employees in the background of his call, chattering and laughing.

Nevertheless, here I was—alone in an empty building, having not seen another person since I left my office.

What had happened to everyone since I put down the phone?

How had it happened so fast?

And why was I left behind?

Quietly panicking now, I briskly walked out the cafeteria and inspected the offices on the second floor again—my eyes flashing from this empty desk to that deserted chair.

No one had taken their stuff: briefcases, papers, phones, jackets, what have you—all were exactly where you would expect them to be if everyone was still at work. I even saw hot vapor rising from a cup of tea on my chief's desk. It wasn't remotely close to the lunch hour, yet the building was even more empty than it would have been then.

As I thought about what to do now, I felt a pressure build in my bladder from drinking tea the whole morning.

Well, first thing's first, I told myself, and stepped into the executive restroom opposite my chief's office.

When I stepped out of the bathroom, there wasn't a blast of light.

No strange bell or noise.

No clap.

But regardless, everything changed—suddenly and dramatically—as if I'd stepped through a portal into a different world.

One minute nothing. The next, a wave of sound crashed against me: colleagues in the hallway standing and talking and laughing before our upcoming meeting or walking there.

I looked at my chief's office. Unlike before, his door was open. Two colleagues were walking from it, followed by several other people, obviously headed to the cafeteria. I grabbed one. "Where were you all?" I said. "Where did you just come from?"

My colleague was shocked by the question. "Huh? What? We are coming from the chief's office, obviously."

What could I say? I had no idea what had just happened. I smiled, nodded, and filed into the meeting along with everyone else.

Of course, I didn't hear a single word during the meeting. I spent the whole time trying to figure out what had taken place. Besides my having somehow stepped into a parallel universe, I had no other explanation.

One particular thought kept nagging me though. What if I hadn't gone to the restroom? Would I have missed my opportunity to return to my world? Would I have remained lost in an empty building forever? Had other people become lost in such a way, and so disappeared mysteriously from our world?

PENCIL BOX

BING JIA

My aunt has a trick for finding lost objects, which she calls "wandering sheep," when retracing your steps doesn't work.

First, relax—through taking a walk, doing household chores, breathing exercises, etc. Once relaxed, next think about things that make you feel happy and grateful, immersing yourself in that feeling, and then say out loud "there you are, wandering sheep." As you say this, feel love and gratitude toward your object and remember all the times it has brought you happiness. Soak in these feelings for a while.

All that's left to do after this step is to turn you mind to other things, less worrying things, and let the Tao do its thing. When you least expect it, what you lost will frequently turn up in a place you already checked or in some impossible, even ridiculous place.

The following account reminded me of aunt's advice. —YIY

When I was in second grade, my deskmate borrowed a pencil from me during our first class period. After she returned it, I carefully put it back in the pencil case on my desk.

Everyone kept their pencil cases on their desks in those days. Not only did they hold your pencils but also your eraser, scissor, sharpener, ruler, etc., and so they were as indispensable as your books.

Anyway, when my second class period started, I looked down and saw that my case was gone.

"What did you do with my pencil case?" I asked my deskmate, thinking she was playing a trick.

"I didn't touch it," she told me. "Why would I? I gave the pencil I borrowed back to you already."

She was right. I remembered her handing it back. And I also remembered putting the pencil back into the case when she did.

With a rising sense of panic, I looked all around my desk and scanned the floor of the classroom in every direction, but there was no sign of my pencil case.

And so at the end of the school day, having no other choice, I had to go home without it—even though it held all the essentials I needed to do my homework that night.

The whole way home, I mentally prepared myself to be scolded by my mother for losing the case. But that's not what happened.

Before I had a chance to confess to *losing* the case, my mother started yelling at me for *forgetting* it.

"What kind of student forgets to bring their pencil case to school?" she asked, jabbing her finger at our bookcase.

I looked where she was pointing and there, on the top of our bookshelf, was my pencil case!

I immediately told her what really happened, of course. But she didn't believe me and accused me of lying to avoid getting into trouble for forgetting the case.

Although many years have passed, I still remember this whole incident clearly. I'm not sure why this change in reality took place. I was scolded and blamed just as I expected, just for a different reason.

THE SECOND PERSON IN THE BOAT

CI KE

When I was about six, I went to bed one night especially excited because the new season of my favorite cartoons was going to premiere the next day.

When I woke up the following morning, I grabbed a bowl of Cheerios cereal and ran into our living room to watch them on our old Zenith TV. After a couple of hours of laughing my head off, I got up for a bathroom break. I had just passed the hallway separating the living room from the kitchen when the craziest thing happened. I found myself waking up in my bed!

You see, I hadn't actually been watching cartoons for the last several hours. I just dreamed I did. But here's the strangest thing of all. Minutes later, when I repeated the actions of the dream I had (in the real world this time), the new cartoon episodes were exactly the same.

This taught me that strange things happen in dreams sometimes. The story below shows this too. —JYB

The following happened when I had just begun elementary school and was about six years old.

One week, my cousin (she is four years older than me so she was around ten) stayed at my home, and we shared a bed. At this point, my family lived in a house we built ourselves in our village. It had a small courtyard, surrounded by stone walls and a big red gate.

Anyway, almost every night that week I had the same dream—the kind where you know that you're dreaming.

In this dream, it was night. I walked through our gate and stood at the side of the wide, concrete road that passed through our village in real life.

Except in my dream it wasn't a road anymore.

It was a dark river. A deep one too.

The whole atmosphere of the dream was depressing and odd. I wanted to escape it. And so when I saw that there was a small wooden boat bobbing in the river, I climbed in and started to row.

Almost as soon as I sat in the boat, I sensed someone in it with me. But I couldn't manage to see them and so ignored that feeling to concentrate on rowing out of the gloom.

However, no matter how much I rowed, I never could reach a lighter part of the river. For the whole dream, I just kept rowing and rowing.

Although it was kind of odd to have the same dream repeatedly, I never told anyone about it and didn't think it was very important until near the end of my cousin's stay. That was when she told me that for the past few days she had been having a weird dream.

As she shared the details of her dream: a walk through a

gate to the road that was a river; climbing into a small wooden boat; a second person in the boat who was felt but impossible to see—I realized that she was describing the exact same dream I had been having.

There was just one big difference.

I was the unseen second person in her dream while she was the unseen second person in mine. I wonder to this day how it was possible for us to have the same dream.

THE BIRD'S NOD

SIYI TONG

My mom and her mother both believe that birds can sense certain things about people and will only build their nests at the home of someone who is at peace and has a bright future. So, whenever they find a bird nest in the bushes near our home or on one of our window ledges, they get very excited. They feel like the bird feels good about our family and its future. I like the story below because it shows how incredible birds can be and how underestimated they are sometimes. —YIY

When I was six or seven years old, just like other kids who lived in the country, I liked to catch chickens, chase dogs, and poke around in nests looking for eggs and baby birds. One afternoon, I was playing outside before dinner and actually found a baby bird. It wasn't in a nest though. It was tangled in an old piece of net that someone had left in the woods next to my village.

The bird was a bulbul bird. I could tell by the white hair on its head. And I could also tell that it was a baby because it was smaller and chubbier than other bulbul birds I'd seen. Excited, I freed it and ran to my nainai's house with it cupped in my hands.

Nainai of course saw what I was holding immediately. "Poor little thing," she said, staring down. "Look at it. It's still a baby. If you keep playing with it, you're going to kill it. And then its mother and father will be too heartbroken to live. Why don't you sell it to me for two yuan instead, and I'll let it go?"

I didn't have to think this over long. Two yuan was a lot of money. Especially to do a thing that was right to begin with.

"Deal," I said.

Nainai set the bird down, and it hopped on the ground outside a few times then flew away. After that, Nainai went to mess with her garden. Suddenly, I heard her yelling. "Come here and look!" she cried. "Look there!"

I sprang up and ran outside to see what was going on. As I rushed through the door, Nainai pointed. "It's the little bird," she said. "It came back with its parents to show you gratitude."

I looked up to the roof where she was pointing. It was for sure the same fat-bodied, white-headed bird I'd caught. Except now two much larger birds were standing on either side of it so that there was a row of three birds, with about ten centimeters between each of them.

When they saw me, the birds turned slightly in my direction. Then incredibly they began BOWING over and over.

Not a twitch, not a slight response to my presence. But an

actual bow, a coordinated one at that, just like a group of human beings might make to show gratitude.

Language is too limited to describe the wonder I felt in that moment. Those three birds, who should not have been making identical movements like that (For how often do birds do such a thing?), those birds who most people thought incapable of even simple reasoning, nevertheless stood there—side by side—and rhythmically bowed at me for more than a minute.

If a bird is capable of such things, shouldn't every form of life fill us with awe?

THE SUBSTITUTE

LAN DE

You come across the concept of using a "substitute" a lot in Chinese culture—especially when it comes to magic and the supernatural. For example, you can deliver goods, presents, and cash to the dead by burning paper replicas of these objects. And one of the most feared ghosts is "the substitute ghost," which tricks a living person into killing themselves in the same way that brought about the ghost's demise. Many other sorts of substitutes are used in magical ceremonies as well, in order to transfer luck, love, and fate. Something like this happens in the story below. —YIY

Ever since he was a kid, my big uncle has always been a partier and a bit of a troublemaker.

Even as an adult, he would stay out all night, socializing and getting rowdy instead of helping take care of the elderly relatives at home. Sometimes he would even be gone for whole days.

My grandfather, along with the older relatives, felt helpless about this situation. But ultimately his attitude was that as long as Big Uncle was okay, and everybody at home was getting by, then there was no reason to make too big a fuss. Still, sometimes Grandfather got worried, and he would take out his *I Ching* fortune-telling manual and throw coins to check on Big Uncle's welfare.

One afternoon as he was doing this, his face suddenly changed, and he leapt up and started calling Big Uncle's friends on the phone in an attempt to track him down.

Soon he got a location. But this information made him more upset, and he asked my mother to go collect Big Uncle and bring him home.

Before my mother was out of the door, my grandfather changed his mind.

No, no, he said, it was too late now. My mother wouldn't arrive in time.

He then ran to his room with the coins and the *I Ching* book, shouted at everyone to stay away, and locked his door.

In no time at all though, he burst out again. "Grab a piece of your brother's clothing and a rooster," he told my mother.

By this point, my mother was very confused. But Grandfather sounded so worried and certain about what he was saying that she did as asked without questions.

Once he had the items, Grandfather took down an old Tai Chi sword from the wall (it had been passed down in the family for generations and was kept around as an heirloom) and killed the screaming rooster right there in his room.

It was a horrible scene.

Blood splattered on his clothes and face and dripped all

over the floor, as he poured the rooster's blood on my uncle's shirt and then waved the body around his room to form a circle of red. Afterwards, he tossed the corpse by our front gate and hurried back to the house for my uncle's bloody shirt. This he carried all the way to the entrance of the village, where he set it on fire and murmured strange words as it burnt.

When finished, Grandfather looked pale and exhausted. He asked my mother to help him back to the house. When they got there, he said to her, "Wait for your brother. When he gets home, lead him to my room and make him kneel at the threshold. Have him stay there until I wake up." Grandfather then went to his room and fell asleep.

My mother waited anxiously in the yard until dark. Finally, she saw my uncle limping toward her, covered in blood, with his face and one leg badly injured.

Big Uncle told my mother that while he was out drinking, a stranger harassed a friend's girlfriend and my uncle's group gave him a good beating.

Everybody at my uncle's table thought the situation was over then. But the harasser got a bunch of *his* friends. Armed with knives and clubs, these thugs came back to the bar for revenge.

The two groups fought. The harasser's group was larger, better armed, and much less drunk. And as their injuries piled up, my uncle and his friends realized they'd made a mistake by taking on the other group and ran away.

The thugs though were angry that some of them had been hurt. So they chased my uncle's group, causing it to split.

My uncle and the boyfriend of the woman found an alley

full of garbage and hid behind some of it. But the thugs quickly found the alley and started searching it, one of them talking very loudly the whole time about how he was going to kill the first person he found.

This was a very scary moment for my uncle. Especially when the thug making the threats discovered him and immediately whipped out a knife.

My uncle thought he was dead then for sure.

He almost was.

But the boyfriend of the harassed woman jumped out and bashed an empty wine bottle across the thug's head, and the knife intended for my uncle sank into his chest instead.

Even though the thug was the perpetrator, he was as shocked by this as my father. He put his hands to the sides of his head and, crying "oh no, oh no," ran off into the night.

My uncle checked his friend for signs of life. Not finding any, he called an ambulance. A few hours later, he left the hospital for home, where he arrived bloody and injured like my mom found him.

To this day, I have no doubt that my grandfather managed to make it so that a substitute took on the fate originally meant for my uncle.

TIME STOPS UNDER MY FEET

YUAN JUNLIN

Life is filled with deadly "almosts." Moments in which something terrible "almost" happens. I know I've had a lot.

One hot day, I was playing hide-and-go-seek in an abandoned lot and climbed in an old refrigerator someone had dumped. I didn't know it at the time, but you can't open a refrigerator from the inside. When my friends hadn't found me after fifteen minutes, I tried to reopen the sealed door. It wouldn't budge. I tried again. It still wouldn't open. I kicked it. Nothing. That's when I really started to panic—kicking, hollering, twisting and wildly throwing my shoulder against the door, feeling increasing faint all the while as my air ran out.

Since the refrigerator was on an abandoned lot, I have no doubt that I would have suffocated to death that day if my classmate's father didn't happen to take a shortcut through the lot and hear my muffled screams while I still had enough air to scream.

Almost car wrecks.

Almost falls in the bathtub.

Somehow our luck saves us from "almost" every time. Sometimes though we need some extra help. And sometimes we get it. —JYB

S ome years of a person's life are filled with strange events. 2006 was that year for me.

One day in November, I got off work to find it raining hard, so I popped open my umbrella. Then, with it low and close to my face, and my headphones on and loudly playing music, I walked as quickly as I could to the road that I needed to cross to get home (Please avoid ever blinding yourself like this).

Since there were no traffic lights on this road, and no one was around whose swishing legs I could follow across, I stopped at the edge to glance around for traffic.

Through my ridiculously small window of visibility, I saw no vehicles approaching, and so I lifted my foot from the sidewalk to step onto the road just like I had hundreds of times before.

But just as my foot lifted, reached its high point, and hovered over the asphalt, it suddenly froze. I mean REALLY froze.

Time had literally stopped.

By this, I don't mean it stopped everywhere. That was maybe the weirdest part. It was as if a bubble of different space-time had formed around my body, and just my body. The world outside continued to operate at a normal speed. So did the thoughts in my head. But my body—one leg high—moved incredibly slow, just short of motionless, so that I felt like a photograph of an action shot, perfectly balanced and fixed in place even while the rain still bounced around me at normal speed.

I struggled as hard as I could to free myself from this immobility. But I couldn't. Not until several moments later, when a Chang'an minivan suddenly rushed past my face, so close that it knocked the umbrella out of my hand, shocking me senseless.

Only then was I freed from my stasis, a stasis that I now understood had just miraculously saved my life.

What or who stopped me in that crucial moment?

What or who stopped time?

After that day, I keep the volume of my music low when I'm near a road.

PEACH WOOD

YING LIN

China's one-child policy dramatically affected a whole generation of parents and kids. For example, as a girl growing up in the 1980s, I always knew that my parents originally wanted a boy, especially my dad, although he deeply loved me once I was born.

Because of this, I always consciously tried to do more around the house as a child, thinking that might compensate them a little for my being a girl. I'd help fix windows and electronics. And whenever needed, I'd carry heavy things like I imagine a boy would have. I looked and dressed like a boy too. Due to my neutral appearance, when people first met me, some of them couldn't even tell if I was a girl or not. At least not until I went to college.

Of course, the "one-child policy" was much bigger than my personal situation. It resulted in millions of forced abortions. Local governments would force women to abort a second child if they found out about it— even if the fetus was 7 or 8 months old.

The worst thing though was some of the dark decisions that parents themselves made. Sometimes, they'd abandon girl babies in the street.

Others drowned babies in the rivers and creeks, so that it wasn't unusual in some villages to see a dead baby float by. A missing child or a dead one, you see, meant you could report that child as kidnapped or accidentally killed. This would free you up to receive government permission to have another go at having a boy. These are very terrible things. But some people committed even more terrible deeds, as the following account shows. —YIY

~

One day while on patrol, my partner and I came across a baby abandoned in front of some shops. We took it to a temporary government shelter and then sat down for a rest. After about a minute, my partner lit a cigarette, turned to me, and told the following story:

"Believe it or not, this is not the first abandoned baby I've found. In fact, the previous case was far more heartbreaking. It happened back in 2009 when I was a rookie at a station in the north.

"The baby belonged to a couple who lived in the suburbs of J city. It was their first child, and they had high hopes when it was born. But the doctor told two things after the delivery that changed their mind. One, the child was a girl and not the son they hoped for. Two, the girl had a heart defect and would likely not live long.

"Since the government would only allow you to have one child at this time, a disabled child was a huge disappointment to some people. So was having a girl. Girls couldn't carry on the family name or get the same jobs as men, they reasoned.

This attitude was even prevalent in the villages of the north, where people mostly made their living through heavy labor and farming.

"That was why when the baby's parents found out that not only did their baby have a severe disease but was a girl, they decided to leave her in a field and pretend as if she'd never been born. That way they'd be free to have another child.

"Because this was a big decision, the couple talked it over with their whole family. One of the child's grandfathers didn't like their plan at all.

"Waving everyone silent, the grandfather said, 'You are not dealing with this matter in a correct way. If you just abandon the child without performing the proper rites, its soul will curse us after it dies. This will doom you and later children.'

"The couple asked what they should do.

"'You don't have to do anything,' said the grandfather. 'I'll do what needs to be done.'

"The grandfather left the apartment. A while later, he returned with a small bag of items, tucked the baby girl under his arm, and left again.

"He did not go far.

"A mountain slope extended from the back of the family's housing complex up into a forested area. The grandfather hiked into this area for almost a mile and chose a tree.

"This done, he braced the baby girl against the tree with his forearm, while using his hands to take a peach wood nail and a hammer out of his bag.

"Before the baby registered what was happening, the grandfather nailed one of her tiny arms to the tree.

"He repeated this with her other arm, then each leg, as the baby shrieked with pain.

"Badly injured but not yet dead, the baby convulsed against the tree like a pinned butterfly. Yet the grandfather did not try to comfort her. Instead, he took a bottle of dog's blood out of the bag and poured it over her head. As it streamed down her body, it mixed with her own blood.

"After this, there was just one final thing to do.

"The grandfather positioned the long, sharp tooth of a black dog right over the baby's heart and hammered it in as deep as it would go.

"Within seconds, the baby fell still. The grandfather put a finger against her tiny nostrils to make sure she was dead. When satisfied that she was, he stepped away from the tree and took one last, long look at his granddaughter.

"Later, he told the police that he felt a wonderful sense of peace in that moment.

"*Peach wood.*

"*Dog blood.*

"*Black dog's tooth.*

"The grandfather believed that individually each of these protected you from curses. And together he was sure they were unbeatable, and that neither he nor the rest of his family would be punished for his deed.

"But what the grandfather didn't reckon on was this: you can't fight a curse if you are the curse. You can't fight evil if you are the evil. And what the grandfather did violated tiandao (天道)—the way of heaven.

"This could not go unpunished.

"Thus, the baby girl didn't die, despite all the torture and the black dog tooth in her heart. Some time after the grandfather left, she stirred again and started crying. She kept this up until late the next morning when a hiker heard her. He called the police. It was only after they arrived and bore witness to what had been done that she allowed herself to die for good.

"For months, this case was all anyone could talk about. It was like a dark shadow over our hearts. Whoever heard the details that the grandfather confessed could not get them out of their minds. Several people were so curious that they even walked near the spot where the grandfather went up the mountain. But everyone refused to stand near the tree itself. They knew the earth couldn't help but be cursed by such an evil deed.

"Despite the horror of his act, however, the grandfather initially avoided prison. The unit that oversaw sentencing argued that the baby would not have survived long anyway, and the parents refused to file charges. So the grandfather was charged with the much lesser crime of child abandonment. This simply involved paying a fine.

"The whole town revolted against this miscarriage of justice though, and eventually a higher level of government intervened. They ordered the local police to treat the case as homicide. Consequently, the grandfather was sentenced to prison for a very long time."

My partner's story shocked me to my core. That a grandfather could do such a thing to his infant granddaughter boggled my mind. From that day forward, whenever I saw peach wood I would think of the little girl. I would think about how she must have felt while nailed to that tree—the victim of a betrayal by those who were supposed to love her. The intensity of her hurt and terror was probably what allowed her to transcend the laws of nature and stay alive long enough to make the wrong done to her known.

MIRROR, MIRROR

YOU DUO

I still have bad dreams about high school. I sit down to take a test and don't know the answers. Or a teacher tells me that I'm flunking. When I wake up and realize that I'm not in high school anymore, I feel so good! High school in China is intense beyond imagination. Teachers constantly spy on you to catch you looking away from your books. Even if it's just for a few seconds, this can be considered slacking off, and the teacher will silently march to your desk and tap their fingernails against it.

And then there's the long hours. Chinese high schools run from 6:30 in the morning to 5:30 at night. And THEN after regular school is done, it's common to have a mandatary, teacher-supervised night study session that goes from 6:30pm to 9:30pm. So while school grounds are empty at night in the West, in China the school campus is filled with exhausted students, unless there's a holiday. These dark nights are mostly safe. But sometimes things happen. —YIY

I once saw another me in the same room.

I was attending a boarding high school then. And after an especially boring night study session, I fled back to my ten-person dormitory room. My roommates always lingered after study sessions to chat with friends so I felt confident I could get at least five minutes to myself if I hurried back.

Since I was the first one through the door, the room lights were off. I flicked them on, threw my schoolbag on the bed, and took a hand mirror out of my personal wardrobe to examine my face. I was really big into checking my face in high school. Most days, I inspected it dozens of times—searching for zits or messy hair.

Anyway, as I was inspecting my face, I suddenly had the creepy feeling that someone else was in the room. Sure enough, when I looked around using my peripheral vision, I saw a person. I could tell by their shape that it was a girl like me.

The girl was standing on our balcony, the door of which was flung open—although it had been closed when we left.

I could see the girl's profile clearly because the balcony had its own little light, and it was switched on, illuminating her. She had no idea I was checking her out though. This was because she was busy doing exactly what I was doing in that moment. Or a version of it anyway. She was looking at her face in a mirror that was dangling from a string attached to the balcony roof like a wind chime and messing around with her short hair.

Now, you should know all of this happened really fast—seconds really. Me switching on the light, throwing down my stuff, examining my reflection in a hand mirror and then

seeing someone on our balcony also looking at herself—
through the mirror we had out there.

But who was this other person?! As my heart pounded, that
was the question I asked myself.

Only my roommates and I had a key to the room. And the
room had been empty when we left. Since it was impossible
for any of my roommates to have beaten me home, the girl *had*
to be a stranger. A stranger who had somehow rushed into
our room after I opened the door.

But how could that have happened? I would have noticed
someone rushing in, would have noticed them running past
the three bunk beds in the room on their way to the balcony.
Even if I somehow had missed all this, I would have certainly
heard them opening the rusty and squeaky balcony door and
flicking on the light.

While I was thinking all this, the girl turned slightly, and I
gasped when I got a really good look at the front of her face.
She was me!

Clothes, hair, shoes, face, ears, everything me.

And what horrified me most wasn't that I was looking at
myself across the room. It was the question in my head: If that
girl over there is "you," then who is the "you" right here?

As soon as this question formed in my mind, I felt very
floaty. It was then that one of my roommates came back. I
heard her yelling my name. The voice was faint, as if from far
away, but I focused on it. As I did, I could vaguely see her
flashing me a puzzled look. I was so in shock that I tried to
speak but couldn't.

"What's with you?" she said loudly. "I've been calling your
name. You've been standing there ignoring me and looking at

your dumb mirror. Are you so addicted to your own face that you can't hear another person talking to you?"

The annoyance in her voice somehow cleared my vision. My hearing too. It was as if I'd returned from some fuzzy and silent, otherworldly place.

I looked back toward the balcony.

The doors were locked.

The lights were off too.

And of course there was no other "I" there.

I still think about what happened on that night. I can't begin to explain it. I never had anything like a hallucination in my whole life. I didn't even have a vivid imagination. Since I was a high schooler, the memory is close enough to today that I remember every detail, unlike the memories you have from when you're a little kid. But that makes no difference. No detail hints at what happened in that room or reveals what might have happened if my roommate hadn't returned.

Maybe what occurred is an example of what people mean when they talk about the soul splitting from the body.

BALLPOINT PEN

LIANG LIANG

The following story deals with a blessed object. These are commonly found across China. To some Chinese people, a blessed object is a ridiculous idea. Others though feel that in blessing an object, one can charge it with divine energy similar to how one can charge a battery or magnetize a piece of metal. And so one finds many objects and even electronic apps being sold that have been allegedly blessed in this way. —YIY

M y grandmother was a Buddhist. Every year she would stay with a few friends in the Buddhist temple for a couple of days to fast.

One year, when I was around six or seven years old, she was on her way back from the temple after her usual retreat when she met a Taoist.

The Taoist came up to my grandmother, waving a ballpoint pen around and talking about how it was blessed. He told her she should buy it.

My grandmother took the pen and examined it closely. It was the very cheap kind that's barely worth two cents. It did not look blessed or in any way special.

It was holy though, insisted the Taoist. And he told my grandmother that sooner or later she'd be happy she bought it. "The power it's charged with is going to save your family from disaster," he said. "You'll see."

Although Taoists and Buddhists do not belong to the same school of religion, they believe a lot of the same things about how the world works. So eventually the Taoist's words convinced my grandmother, and she handed over 150 yuan [about 20 dollars] to him.

When she got home, the rest of my family teased my grandmother and said that she must not have been thinking straight to let a Taoist scam her like that. But my grandmother shrugged off their words and gave me the pen as a gift.

"Work hard in school," she told me.

I promised her that I would.

But then the next day, when I took the pen to school, I discovered that it could not even write. 150 yuan for a ballpoint pen that was too broken to manage a single word!

After school, I put the pen in my pocket and started off for home, where I planned to report to my mom that the Taoist was definitely a swindler. On my way, I met up with a classmate who begged me to go to his place to hang out. Since he lived close, I agreed.

Right off the start, things were very strange at his house.

My classmate's grandmother acted more shocked by my visit than she should have been. And then she poured me a drink that had a strange color. All this made me nervous, and I shoved my hands in my pockets to rub my fingers together. This is something I do when I'm anxious. But I had forgotten that the pen was in one pocket. Its tip instantly pierced my palm and made it bleed.

Now, when I was little, any kind of bleeding scared me badly, so I immediately ran out of my friend's house to buy a band-aid at a nearby store. I planned to return to my friend's house after bandaging my palm, but on the way back I ran into my mom who was getting off from work.

"What have I told you about going directly home after school?" she said and dragged me there.

At school the next day, I looked for my friend to apologize for not returning.

But he wasn't there.

Later that night, I learned a very terrible thing. My friend, his younger brother, and his grandmother were all dead.

My friend's grandmother turned out to be mentally ill, and sometimes she had spells. Since the family did not have a lot of money, they left her illness untreated—thinking it was not such a big deal. On the day I visited though, she had one of her spells. It was worse than anyone thought possible—because she poisoned the drinks of my classmate and his brother with pesticides.

After they died, the grandmother carried their heavy bodies, one after the other—as if they were sleeping in her arms—to a cliffside field on the outskirts of the village. She pushed them off the cliff. And then she jumped off too, ending her life.

This incident is famous in our small town to this day. Although it took place a long time ago, I still feel frightened when I think of it. If I hadn't gone to the store to get a band-aid, I'd be dead too. The ballpoint pen really saved my life.

I know the whole thing is unbelievable to most people. If it hadn't happened to me, I know I would not believe it. It's been a lot of years now since my grandmother passed away. During her life, she always tried to be kind and do good things for other people. I'm heavily influenced by her to be kind and humble too. I don't totally buy into all her Buddhist beliefs, but they do awe me because they meant so much to her. Maybe one of these beliefs explains how a cheap, fake-seeming blessed pen could hold power. Maybe not. Anyhow, what happened happened. Make of it what you will.

I have attached my grandparents' photos. The child is the first photo is not me but a neighbor. The second photo is a picture of my palm. The blue dot is the place where the pen poked me. The mark is still there after all these years.

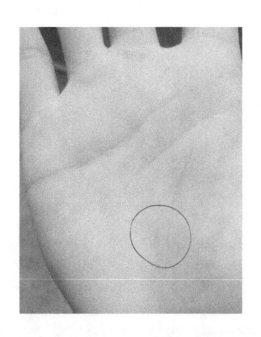

WHITE LIGHT MAN

MAN LI

In ancient Chinese tales, one frequently comes across figures emitting bright white light. Usually, this is due to their cultivation of the primal, reality-creating energy known as qi. Much like the Jedi in Star Wars (figures inspired by ancient Chinese tales), these Taoist masters learned to use and accumulate qi, and this allowed them to perform all kinds of miraculous feats—teleportation, bending time, immortality, resurrection, you name it. The following story recalls these figures and makes one deeply curious about the mysterious stranger at the heart of the story. —JYB

I'm going to share something with you that happened when I was a kid, and my family was living in a small village.

One afternoon, my mom was playing mahjong at a neighbor's. After a while, I started to miss her so I walked over to the neighbor's, whose home was very close, to check on her.

No big deal.

At least it wasn't until I encountered a man outside my neighbor's courtyard gate. The man was so deeply odd that I froze in my tracks.

He looked to be in his 20s, and his whole body was covered in white light. Not only that, but as he passed by the courtyard gate, he rapidly flickered—as if a glitching frame in a video game.

Sensing the man, the neighbor's dog came charging out about the same time I saw him, barking her head off.

The man visibly reacted to her but acted even more alarmed when he noticed me from his peripheral vision. Immediately, he spun in my direction.

As soon as he was facing me, I saw that his expression was anxious, as if he was in the middle of an emergency. I noticed too that his clothes were strange—not the simple, plain ones popular when I was a kid but more like the brightly colored kind people wear today.

Our eyes locked for a brief second, then the man fled, impossibly quick, disappearing down the alley around the corner of the neighbor's house.

I'm not quite sure how to describe his movement in that moment. It was an odd combination of leaping/sliding/flying away—boneless, mechanical, and digital all at one time. Even this combination falls short of describing exactly what he looked like because I'd never seen anyone move like that before. Nor have I since.

I ran after the man to catch another glimpse, but there was no sign of him anywhere.

When I returned to the neighbor's house, my mom and

the other mahjong players asked me what in the world had set the dog off. I told them. Not one person believed a word I said. I understand not believing a kid when they tell you something that crazy. But when that crazy thing draws the attention of a dog too and makes it go crazy, you should think about being more open-minded.

ID

JIA YI

Accounts like the following, where reality is shuffled around and dramatically altered, are more common than you think. Maybe this shouldn't be such a surprise. After all, quantum physics tells us that consciousness affects reality, especially those parts of reality that are observed by just one person or a few people. In fact, there are many reports of small pieces of our world being caught in the act of changing. The following is one of them. —YIY

A few months ago, in June 2018, my mother saw my ID card when I left it out.

"This is about to expire," she told me. "You need a new one."

I was sure my mom was wrong. I applied for my ID card right after my college entrance examination during my senior year of high school. This was 2010. And since such cards last for 10 years, it was clearly impossible for mine to expire after only 8 years.

But when I took the ID card from her, I saw that she was right. The period of validity was clearly stated as lying between July 2008 and July 2018.

Okay, I thought to myself. I guess I remembered wrong, after all. I must have applied for the card very early in high school for some reason.

I made a mental note to get a new ID card soon and pushed the subject to the back of my mind for the time being.

When the ID card came to mind again, I was getting ready to register for a job-related certification exam at the end of that August. Suddenly, I realized that my ID card had now expired, which would prevent me from registering.

Because I was working at a state-owned enterprise, your schedule was negotiable. As long as you gave the manager a good reason, you could even leave work early. So I went to the manager to ask permission to do just that (to be honest, I was happy to have an excuse to leave work early).

After I explained my situation, the manager took my ID card and looked closely at the date to make sure I wasn't trying to get away with something. Like me, he saw that the card was now expired and let me leave.

But what happened next would change how I viewed the world forever after.

A little past four in the afternoon, right before the officers got off work, I arrived at the police station.

A female officer was on duty then. She asked me what I needed.

"To apply for a new ID card since mine has expired," I said.

The officer took my card and gave it a look. She then raised her face and stared at me for a few, uncomfortable seconds. "I don't know why you're saying that this has expired. You actually have two more years on it."

Dumbfounded, I didn't know how to reply. So I silently took back my ID and examined it. The valid period on the reverse side was now listed as July 2010 to July 2020! Just like she said. Just like I originally thought.

I was stunned.

The *same* ID card. The *same* card that my mother checked back in June. That I checked after she called my attention to it. The *same* card that my manager had just checked in order to give me permission to leave early.

It's completely unrealistic to claim that my mom, me, and my manager separately yet collectively hallucinated a different expiration date for my card than was the case. So its validity period had obviously changed back to what I remembered it being when my Mom first brought the matter up.

How?

Why?

I really can't answer these questions.

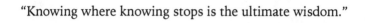

"Knowing where knowing stops is the ultimate wisdom."

—Zhuangzi (369–286 BCE)

INTERVIEW EXCERPTS

What drew you to this project?

A couple of things. We put together a translation of older zhiguai by a very famous Chinese writer, Ji Yun, who wrote a lot of "true" autobiographical paranormal and weird tales back in the eighteenth century. In doing this, we realized that a lot of similar stories were being told by people today. We're talking a similarity rooted both in theme and people's purpose for sharing such stories. We thought this was pretty cool and that gathering together the best examples of modern work would show that a very important kind of Chinese literature was still significant to this day.

Two, we've both had very strange experiences occur in our own lives. By collecting and sharing the experiences of others, we were able to think a bit more about the implications of those experiences.

Finally, we're teachers and both of us, while teaching the history of Chinese strange tales, tasked our students with sharing any strange experiences they might have had. We discovered to their shock and ours that about 1/3 to 1/2 of each of our classes have experienced things that could be classified as paranormal, glitchy, or otherwise weird. This blew our minds and those of our students. In fact, several students told us that it was a big relief to them to discover that others had also had paranormal or glitch experiences, and that this helped them come to terms with theirs.

What's the history of zhiguai in China?

Zhiguai can in part be traced back to the Chinese Taoist philosopher Zhuangzi (369–286 BCE). He coined the term to refer to storytellers of the strange aka: "guai," a word which came to mean a strangeness rooted in a reality radically beyond the everyday, but which is nonetheless claimed to be true by the teller.

Specifically, Zhuangzi discusses a man who tells a "zhiguai" about a cosmically gargantuan fish. We're talking a fish hundreds and hundreds of miles long, with a head so big that your eyes and mind can't fully comprehend it.

To top it off, this fish—the "kun"—periodically transforms into an equally massive bird, the "peng." While readers today would have a hard time accepting such a tale as true, it must have seemed plausible at a time when all kinds of bizarre new creatures were being discovered daily, from blue whales to giant squids. And it established a tradition of tales of strange plants and animals being shared in zhiguai collections alongside supernatural phenomena—plants and animals that when described would fill the reader with awe.

Even more significantly for contemporary world weird literature though, and related literary flavors, Zhuangzi also shares a strange tale of his own: "The Parable of the Butterfly." He doesn't explicitly name it as "zhiguai." Nevertheless, it is China's most famous early weird tale and sets important precedents for zhiguai collections: the inclusion of parables that express metaphorical truths and the inclusion of paranormal dreams.

In Zhuangzi's butterfly parable, he recounts a dream where he is a butterfly. It's a very striking dream to him because it feels as real as his waking human life, although his thought processes and perceptions are specifically those of a butterfly. This seemingly autobiographical parable ends in a trippy way too by Zhuangzi asking the reader what he really is—butterfly or man—and wondering about the distinction that exists between things and about the principles underlying their transformation into one another. It's an amazing work, one that's just as thought-provoking today as it was thousands of years ago. And its basic plot carries over to modern movies like *The Matrix* and anime like *Sword Art Online*, in which a character discovers that they are a virtual reality avatar living in a virtual world. What more can you ask for from weird prose than for it to not just unsettle your sense of reality during your reading but also afterwards?

After Zhuangzi, the term "zhiguai" is consistently used to refer to tales that create an atmosphere and emotional effect of radical strangeness with metaphysical implications, particularly tales that are claimed to be true, literally or allegorically. Some of these are weird in a capital W way, and others are simply weird in a more generic sense—as a synonym for strange, odd, or baffling. These include everything from scientific and botanical anomalies (just think how "weird" a black hole is or quantum physics) to supernatural events. In fact, collections of these tales are classified in libraries as philosophy and history and assembled by historians as a shadow counterpart to their more orthodox work. This was done famously, for example, by the historian Gan Bao (fl. 315 CE). He was inspired to compile a foundational collection of zhiguai after his family had several paranormal experiences in order to explore "shendao" (the ways of spirits).

From Gan Bao on, zhiguai are in most cases united by certain traits. They're strange in a way that shocks open the reader's view of reality. And they're meant to at least attempt to record the true—even if it's the allegorical sort or not 100% verifiable.

This changes roughly around the eleventh century, when zhiguai's entertainment value starts to become more important to some writers than its truth-telling function. Consequently, there's a huge influx of comedic zhiguai, "adult" zhiguai, and other sorts. From that point forward, a debate rages. Should zhiguai be a genre of fiction that entertains by way of strange happenings? Or should they be a genre of nonfiction that cracks open the mind by way of strange, true narratives that make their readers realize the limitations of their understanding of the universe?

Today, this debate is still ongoing. Some people think of zhiguai as any paranormal or supernatural story, true or not true, weird or not, and are indifferent to their truth-telling function. And others, like us, are more interested in zhiguai as a very specific type of creative nonfiction, true tales about destabilizing weird or paranormal events or phenomena that can't be fully understood and which hint that reality is much vaster and mysterious than our conceptions allow.

Where do you most commonly find zhiguai today?

The closest contemporary counterparts to nonfiction zhiguai are "true" glitch-in-the-matrix and paranormal tales. Contemporary zhiguai also include, as the scholar Mingming Liu points out, certain kinds of reality TV shows, like legal or true crime documentaries where a supernatural explanation erupts to the foreground.

Some people as well use the phrase "zhiguai fiction" to refer to fictional Chinese paranormal tales. Those can be found everywhere, from online games to comics and anime.

Additionally, there are also two related terms that you'll come across pretty frequently in horror circles in China. "Guai qi" and "guai tan" are used to refer specifically to Lovecraftian weird fiction. This is a very popular genre across East Asia, thanks in part to the work of Junji Ito, the popularity of H.P. Lovecraft and Franz Kafka, and of course the long tradition of zhiguai.

We think this whole conversation about terms is very cool and exciting. Through it, many Chinese lit folks are thinking very hard about what to call Chinese weird fiction and about what might define it, as well as related genres. They are also adding to a more general, global conversation about horror, weird, and paranormal creative nonfiction. The creative nonfiction part of the conversation is very timely given that current memoirs like Carmen Maria Machado's *In the Dream House* and Augusten Burroughs' *Toil and Trouble* are exploring this territory. And it's a very revolutionary way to think about creative nonfiction—while being at the same time a return to something that was long prized in Chinese culture.

Weird fiction and nonfiction are both found the world over. Is there anything that makes Chinese weird nonfiction or fiction unique?

Absolutely. The intrusion of an external and threatening strangeness beyond human reason into our everyday world, which partially defines the weird as a genre, and the ensuing sense of ontological instability and epistemological uncertainty, which partially defines it as an aesthetic effect, are in a Chinese context marked by Taoist and Buddhist metaphysics, as well as by China's shamanic roots.

Thus, in the Chinese weird (as well as in related genres) we see a variety of metaphysical principles and ideas play out: the constant transformation of things, which is rooted in a view of reality as incessantly in flux; "ganying" (a supernatural resonance and interconnection between distant things and structures); "renfu tianshu" (a resonance and mirroring between otherworldly or "higher" dimensions and humanity); "ming" (fate); the law of karma; "yūgen" (or 幽玄, an originally Chinese Taoist and Buddhist term that connotes the deep, mysterious, elusive, and wistful beauty of a reality that ever exceeds our mind); Buddhist ideas about the inexpressibility and emptiness of ultimate reality, as well as the illusory nature of the visible world; a belief in fu talismans and sigils and other magical paraphernalia and practices that erase the mind/matter and symbolic/literal divide; and an embrace of both/and thinking. Additionally, one typically sees too in the Chinese weird qualities highly prized in Chinese literary art:

an artistic use of silence, space, suggestiveness, and a narrative gesture that could be called koanic—in which the reader is moved to radically reframe their sense of self and reality through exposure to strange uses of language and irrational gestures.

How much of zhiguai are "weird" in an H.P. Lovecraft or Junji Ito sense, versus just being weird in a way that is a synonym for odd, strange, or paranormal?

Well, first off people have very different ideas sometimes about how to define the weird versus say the uncanny, the strange, the cosmic, the sublime, and so on. But, in general, that depends on how a particular author treats zhiguai. For those who just treat zhiguai as paranormal comedy or satire, very little. However, you'll find a lot of this very specific kind of weirdness in zhiguai intended as nonfiction. Zhiguai which, in other words, go back to the genre's roots. This material after all frequently claims that the actual world we live in exceeds the ability of our everyday reason to grasp it and, further, claims that our world is full of unseen threats and invisible dimensions. This can't help but fill one with that special blend of dread, angst, and awe that marks cosmic horror and other flavors of the weird. The upside of this of course is it makes the world way cool.

*Thanks to Sarah Dodd of *Samovar* and Monica Kuebler of *Rue Morgue Magazine* for the interview opportunities from which some of the above materials are excerpted.

DISCUSSION QUESTIONS

1. What are some of the strangest things that have happened to you or members of your family?
2. What are the weirdest things you believe? Do you believe in reincarnation or ghosts, for example? Why or why not?
3. What's the scariest thing that has happened to you?
4. Pick any one of the stories in this collection and think about the different reasons that might explain what occurs in it.
5. What's the strangest dream you ever had?
6. What experiences in your life have most changed how you understand yourself or the world?
7. Which story in this collection was the scariest for you and why?
8. What questions does this collection leave you asking? What topics does it lead you to want to know more about?
9. What's something that amazes you?
10. Share something secret that you have not shared with anyone before.

TRANSLATOR BIOGRAPHIES

About Yi Izzy Yu

In 2011, Yi Izzy Yu left Northern China for the US, with nothing but $500 in her pocket and a love of Chinese horror and paranormal stories that she'd inherited from her grandmother. Since then, she has acquired a PhD in Composition and Applied Linguistics, taught Chinese and English in high schools and universities, DJ'ed a radio show on K-pop, and married John Yu Branscum. Her work has appeared in such magazines as *Strange Horizons-Samovar*, *New England Review*, *Passages North*, *Dusie*, and *Cincinnati Review*, been nominated for awards ranging from the Year's Best Microfiction to Sundress Publications' Best of the Net, and has placed as a finalist for the international [Gabriel García Márquez] "Gabo" Award for Translation and Multilingual Literature. Currently, she lives outside of Pittsburgh, where she teaches and translates Chinese and investigates shadows.

About John Yu Branscum

Troubled teen turned college professor, John Yu Branscum had a mystical awakening outside a barn in Shepherdsville, Kentucky one night that eventually led to his abandoning a life of crime and becoming a professor of Comparative Literature and Creative Writing. His creative work has won a number of awards, ranging from the Ursula LeGuin Award for Imaginative Fiction to the Linda Bruckheimer Award for Literature, but most significantly his poetry played a major role in helping him woo his wife Yi Izzy Yu. He enjoys lucid dreaming and meditation, Asian horror, manga, comics, jiu jitsu, making REALLY disgusting "smoothies," and durian fruit.

Dear Readers:

If you enjoyed the stories in this collection, please leave a review online somewhere, such as Goodreads or Amazon. We'd love to know how you feel about the individual pieces or the book as a whole. You might also want to check out the weird "sister book" to this collection: *The Shadow Book of Ji Yun: The Chinese Classic of Weird True Tales, Horror Stories, and Occult Knowledge.*

Best regards,

Yi Izzy Yu
John Yu Branscum

An excerpt from

THE SHADOW BOOK OF JI YUN

TWICE GOODBYE

My son Ruchuan's wife, Lady Zhao, was a sensitive and enchanting young woman—one of those people who make you glad to be near them.

My wife Mistress Ma continually boasted to others about Lady Zhao's character and literary talent, as well as her needlework. She said that Lady Zhao talked with such charm that one could happily listen to her for a whole day. This was all true. We could not have hoped for a better daughter-in-law.

So, when Lady Zhao died at only thirty-three years of age, I received a wound that still aches when I think of her. But my pain was nothing compared to what Ruchuan suffered. For many years, he mourned pitifully. Then one year he was ordered to temporarily move to Hubei to undertake some professional duties. While there, he entered a new relationship.

The first time I saw this woman upon Ruchuan's return, I was too shocked to speak. She looked just like Lady Zhao— the shape and length of her limbs, the flicker of her smile, how she moved—everything exactly the same. Ruchuan's coworkers were as stunned as me and drilled him about the woman's relatives and her birth details, suspecting that she was a reincarnation. But it turned out that the woman was born well before Lady Zhao died.

That two women should so resemble one another—down to marrying the same man—is a coincidence with a pulse and meaning. This is especially apparent when you consider their last point of similarity, which is this: only a few months after joining Ruchuan's household, this new woman also died very young and unexpectedly. What can one make of these women's similarities? Why does Heaven copy some things and then introduce them into our lives repeatedly so that we continually meet the same person or experience the same disaster? Surely there is some conclusion we're meant to come to.

GUESTS FROM THE SKY

One day I received a letter that was written in my language but seemed to be written in a foreign one. The thoughts it expressed were odd, confused, and almost impossible to decipher. The letter's poor quality especially surprised me since my friend Shen Tiechan, who was highly intelligent and highly articulate, had written it. The letter was disturbing too because its tone was nostalgic and sorrowful, as if it was written as a final goodbye—this even though I knew that Tiechan had just begun a probationary post in Shanxi.

Not long after that, I received word that there would be no more letters. Tiechan was dead.

Life is filled with strange happenings that are hard to fit into our understanding of the world. Many we let pass in order to get on with our days. But this was not something I could let pass. I talked to Tiechan's neighbors and his friends, his family members and his enemies. Slowly, I pieced together what had pushed my friend to his tragic end. This is what I discovered.

That summer, Tiechan went hunting in the Xian mountains to restore his spirits after a long illness. The hunting trip proceeded unremarkably, with one notable exception: something followed him out of the woods.

This something took the form of two orbs in the sky, turning like windmills. No one else could see the orbs. Even Tiechan didn't see them in the way that one normally sees, which is to say that he could see them when he looked up even if his eyes were closed.

For several days, the orbs silently followed. Then suddenly, without warning, they broke open. From inside two young women emerged, floated down, and delivered a message. Their mistress, a xian nü fairy, wished to meet Tiechan.

Knowing that he could not reject such an invitation, Tiechan agreed to meet the xian nü. Instantaneously, he was transported to a room. It was unlike any he had ever been in. Its dimensions were dizzying, and its massive jade walls were eccentrically decorated with odd purple seashells.

The room's strangeness made Tiechan tremble, but its effect paled compared to the appearance of the xian nü mistress. She was beautiful, yes. But it was not a peaceful kind of beauty. It was the kind of beauty that disturbs because it exceeds limits.

Her words exceeded limits as well. Shocking Tiechan, the xian nü asked him to become her lover.

When he refused, saying that he felt too overwhelmed by his strange surroundings to comply, the xian nü became angry and waved him away. The next thing he knew he was waking up on the road where the xian nü's servants first approached him.

Tiechan hoped that was the end of the matter. But several weeks later, the two rotating spheres reappeared. So, did the two female servants. They did not ask him to come with them this time. They just took him. But they took him to a new place—smaller, homier, less exotic in furnishing and colors. It was much easier on his mind. So, when the xian nü asked Tiechan if he felt more comfortable now, he had no choice but to say yes. This pleased her, and she declared he then no longer had any reason to reject her. He agreed.

From then on, they met regularly—during both waking and dreaming states. "Tell no one," said the xian nü.

Tiechan promised not to and didn't for a long time—not even when he got sick.

But, finally, the severity of his illness convinced him to visit a doctor who specialized in matters of both the spirit and the body. However, it was too late. Tiechan couldn't keep the red pills the doctor prescribed down, nor anything else. Everything was vomited back up. He died during one of these vomiting fits, and his last letter to me was written during these weeks of illness.

I will not forget Shen Tiechan. His qualities were simply too admirable. He wrote poetry that moved the heart and opened the mind. His calligraphy dazzled. He was witty, fun, and generous. However, no one is without secrets or vices, and I discovered one more fact about Tiechan during my investigation—one that might provide a clue to how all the weird events began.

In Tiechan's middle age, he had begun to mourn the passing of his youthful looks and obsess about death. This launched his pursuit of a formula for immortality. He acquired books of occult knowledge and sought out alchemists and sorcerers who were rumored to dabble in forbidden magic. It is no surprise then that something inexplicable occurred that ultimately led to his death. However, it is a shame. While spiritual entities of many kinds exist, they usually won't molest human beings unless a person goes out of their way to make themselves known.

Through my investigations, it seems to me that the manifestations of such entities, and the tragedies that follow in their wake, are prompted not by events in the external world but mysteriously conjured by events in one's internal world: the desires of the heart and what one dares imagine. If only Tiechan had guarded these inner borders better.[1]

---

1. This tale is nearly identical to modern accounts of alien abduction in several respects, from the appearance of a circular sky-craft inhabited by a mating-minded humanoid entity to episodes of teleportation and the infliction of the abductee with a strange illness (which in contemporary accounts would be interpreted as radiation sickness).

MEAT VEGETABLES

When I was boy, I went on a journey with our family servant Shi Xiang. While we were passing a village outside of Jingcheng, Shi Xiang pointed at some mounds in a field to the west. "Those are graves," he said. "Zhou graves. Long ago, one of their ancestors did a good deed that allowed their family line to persist three generations longer than it would have otherwise."

I asked Shi Xiang what kind of deed. He said that the ancestor did not eat a certain piece of meat. He then told me this story, which I now tell you:

As the Ming dynasty limped toward its conclusion and gave over to the Qing when the rule of the Manchus took effect, the Henan and Shandong provinces were decimated by a drought. This drought withered everything to dust. As if the drought wasn't bad enough, a vast swarm of locusts next descended on the provinces.

Many villages died out due to starvation during this time. But a few cursed villages refused to accept extinction. They ate every animal or insect they could catch and scoured every twig or stem of anything edible that the drought and the locusts had not killed off. They even ate the bark and roots of the trees and bushes. When these things ran out, they moved onto each other.

Officials, who had previously spent hours debating the inherent goodness of human nature as put forth by Mencius, or who had enthused about the elegance of Confucian insights into the cultivation of human emotion, did not try to stop this. Instead, they joined in, unable to see the sense of rules of propriety that would see them dead. In this new social order, women and children from the poorest families were sold by relatives or taken by force. They were then bound and gagged and sold at street markets as "cairen"— meat vegetables—an ancient term that occurred in the historical records every couple of centuries in times of extreme hardship.

This was the state of affairs that met a travelling Zhou ancestor when he stopped to rest in the restaurant of a small Shandong village and there ordered a pork dish. At first, the Zhou did not understand what was going on. Then he gave his order to the cook, and the man told him that the kitchen was out of meat.

"Give me a minute though," said the cook, "and I'll cut you up some fresh meat myself." He yelled back to the kitchen, "You're taking too long back there. We have hungry customers. Drag me some pigs out so I can chop off a hoof, and then you can finish the job at your pace."

That was when the Zhou's world turned upside down. Because, after the cook spoke, his assistant dragged out two young women from a back room. They were bound in ropes and gagged.

Before Zhou knew what was going on, the cook grabbed one of the women, dragged her to a butchering area on the kitchen floor, and hacked off her arm with a cleaver. Gushing blood from the fresh stump, the woman flopped and writhed and screamed against her gag. The other customers acted like nothing unusual was going on, but Zhou rushed forward.

Both women saw him. The one with the severed arm cried for him to kill her. The other woman, trembling pitifully with a face drained of all human color, started screaming against her gag too—but her plea was to be saved. Waving money around to buy their freedom, Zhou yelled at the cook to stop cutting and sell him the women's freedom. After he saw how much money the Zhou was offering, the cook agreed.

The first woman had lost too much blood to have a chance at any kind of freedom but the kind she was begging for. So, Zhou plunged a knife into her heart. As for the second woman, she remained by his side as they travelled away from the village. Later, she became his concubine and bore a son. It was this son that allowed the Zhou's line to continue three generations longer than it would have otherwise.

When the midwife wiped the afterbirth from their son, the Zhou and the woman saw that the boy was marked by a bright red line—a birthmark that looked like a cut. It ran from the edge of the baby's armpit and around his shoulder blade—so that it looked exactly like the wound the other woman had sustained. This shows how deeply we are marked not only by the previous lives we've lived, but also by those we've encountered during those previous lives.